xte

Truman Capote
Breakfast at Tiffany's

Herausgegeben von
Herbert Geisen

Philipp Reclam jun. Stuttgart

Diese Ausgabe darf nur in der Bundesrepublik Deutschland, in Österreich und in der Schweiz vertrieben werden.

Universal-Bibliothek Nr. 9241
Alle Rechte vorbehalten
Copyright für diese Ausgabe © 1989 Philipp Reclam jun. GmbH & Co., Stuttgart
Copyright für den Text 1950, 1951, © 1956 by Truman Capote. Renewed 1978, 1979, 1984 by Truman Capote. Renewed 1985 by the Estate of Truman Capote. Renewed 1986 by Alan U. Schwartz.
Die vorliegende Ausgabe erscheint mit Genehmigung von Random House, Inc., New York
Gesamtherstellung: Reclam, Ditzingen. Printed in Germany 1998
RECLAM und UNIVERSAL-BIBLIOTHEK sind eingetragene Marken der Philipp Reclam jun. GmbH & Co., Stuttgart
ISBN 3-15-009241-8

Breakfast at Tiffany's[1]

I am always drawn back to places where I have lived, the
houses and their neighborhoods. For instance, there is a
brownstone in the East Seventies[2] where, during the
early years of the war, I had my first New York apartment. It was one room crowded with attic furniture, a
sofa and fat chairs upholstered in that itchy, particular
red velvet that one associates with hot days on a train.
The walls were stucco, and a color rather like tobacco-
spit. Everywhere, in the bathroom too, there were prints
of Roman ruins freckled brown with age. The single window looked out on a fire escape. Even so, my spirits
heightened whenever I felt in my pocket the key to this
apartment; with all its gloom, it still was a place of my
own, the first, and my books were there, and jars of
pencils to sharpen, everything I needed, so I felt, to
become the writer I wanted to be.

---

4 **brownstone** (AE): für New York City typisches Haus aus rötlich-
   braunem Sandstein.
6 **attic:** Dachboden.
7 **to upholster:** polstern.
   itchy: kratzig.
9 **stucco:** stuckverziert.
9 f. **tobacco-spit:** Tabakspeichel.
10 **print:** Druck, (Kunst-)Reproduktion.
11 **freckled:** hier: gesprenkelt.
12 **fire escape:** Feuertreppe.
   even so: (aber) trotzdem.
   spirits (pl.): Stimmung.
13 **to heighten:** steigen.

It never occurred to me in those days to write about Holly Golightly[3], and probably it would not now except for a conversation I had with Joe Bell that set the whole memory of her in motion again.

5 Holly Golightly had been a tenant in the old brownstone; she'd occupied the apartment below mine. As for Joe Bell, he ran a bar around the corner on Lexington Avenue[4]; he still does. Both Holly and I used to go there six, seven times a day, not for a drink, not always, but to 10 make telephone calls: during the war a private telephone was hard to come by. Moreover, Joe Bell was good about taking messages, which in Holly's case was no small favor, for she had a tremendous many.

Of course this was a long time ago, and until last week I 15 hadn't seen Joe Bell in several years. Off and on we'd kept in touch, and occasionally I'd stopped by his bar when passing through the neighborhood; but actually we'd never been strong friends except in as much as we were both friends of Holly Golightly. Joe Bell hasn't an 20 easy nature, he admits it himself, he says it's because he's a bachelor and has a sour stomach. Anyone who knows him will tell you he's a hard man to talk to. Impossible if you don't share his fixations, of which Holly is one. Some

---

2 **except for ...:** hier: wäre da nicht ... gewesen.
5 **tenant:** Bewohner(in), Mieter(in).
7 **bar:** Bar, Lokal.
11 **to come by** (infml.): (an etwas) herankommen.
12 **to take messages:** (jdm. etwas) ausrichten, Nachrichten entgegennehmen.
13 **tremendous:** unglaublich.
15 **off and on:** ab und zu.
19f. **to have an easy nature:** umgänglich sein.
21 **bachelor:** Junggeselle.
   sour stomach: saurer Magen, nervöse Magenbeschwerden.
23 **fixation:** Fixierung.

others are: ice hockey, Weimaraner dogs, *Our Gal Sunday* (a soap serial he has listened to for fifteen years), and Gilbert and Sullivan[5] – he claims to be related to one or the other, I can't remember which.

And so when, late last Tuesday afternoon, the telephone rang and I heard "Joe Bell here," I knew it must be about Holly. He didn't say so, just: "Can you rattle right over here? It's important," and there was a croak of excitement in his froggy voice.

I took a taxi in a downpour of October rain, and on my way I even thought she might be there, that I would see Holly again.

But there was no one on the premises except the proprietor. Joe Bell's is a quiet place compared to most Lexington Avenue bars. It boasts neither neon nor television. Two old mirrors reflect the weather from the streets; and behind the bar, in a niche surrounded by photographs of ice-hockey stars, there is always a large bowl of fresh flowers that Joe Bell himself arranges with matronly care. That is what he was doing when I came in.

"Naturally," he said, rooting a gladiola deep into the
5 bowl, "naturally I wouldn't have got you over here if it wasn't I wanted your opinion. It's peculiar. A very peculiar thing has happened."

"You heard from Holly?"

He fingered a leaf, as though uncertain of how to answer.
10 A small man with a fine head of coarse white hair, he has a bony, sloping face better suited to someone far taller; his complexion seems permanently sunburned: now it grew even redder. "I can't say exactly heard from her. I mean, I don't know. That's why I want your opinion. Let
15 me build you a drink. Something new. They call it a White Angel," he said, mixing one-half vodka, one-half gin, no vermouth. While I drank the result, Joe Bell stood sucking on a Tums and turning over in his mind what he had to tell me. Then: "You recall a certain
20 Mr. I. Y. Yunioshi? A gentleman from Japan."

"From California," I said, recalling Mr. Yunioshi perfectly. He's a photographer on one of the picture magazines, and when I knew him he lived in the studio apartment on the top floor of the brownstone.

---

1 **bowl:** (Blumen-)Schale, kugelförmige Vase.

2 **matronly:** hier: hausfraulich.

4 **to root:** hier: hineinstecken.

10 **coarse:** hier: wild wachsend.

11 **sloping:** hier: langgezogen.

12 **complexion:** Teint, Gesichtsfarbe.

15 **to build:** hier: (Getränk) mixen.

18 **to suck on s.th.:** an etwas lutschen.

    Tums: Handelsname für eine Magentablette; etwa: Rennie.

19 **to recall s.o.:** sich an jdn. erinnern.

"Don't go mixing me up. All I'm asking, you know who I mean? Okay. So last night who comes waltzing in here but this selfsame Mr. I. Y. Yunioshi. I haven't seen him, I guess it's over two years. And where do you think he's been those two years?"

"Africa."

Joe Bell stopped crunching on his Tums, his eyes narrowed. "So how did you know?"

"Read it in Winchell[6]." Which I had, as a matter of fact. He rang open his cash register, and produced a manila envelope. "Well, see did you read this in Winchell."

In the envelope were three photographs, more or less the same, though taken from different angles: a tall delicate Negro man wearing a calico skirt and with a shy, yet vain smile, displaying in his hands an odd wood sculpture, an elongated carving of a head, a girl's, her hair sleek and short as a young man's, her smooth wood eyes too large and tilted in the tapering face, her mouth wide, overdrawn, not unlike clown-lips. On a glance it resembled most primitive carving; and then it didn't, for here was the spit-image of Holly Golightly, at least as much of a likeness as a dark still thing could be.

---

1 **to mix s.o. up:** jdn. durcheinanderbringen.
2 **to waltz in** (infml.): hereintanzen, hereingetanzt kommen.
7 **to crunch on s.th.** (infml.): auf etwas herumbeißen.
10 **to ring open:** mit einem Klingeln öffnen.
   cash register: Registrierkasse.
   manila: braun (Papierfarbe).
14 **calico:** Kattun.
16 **elongated:** länglich.
   carving: Schnitzerei.
   sleek: glatt.
18 **tilted:** schräg geneigt.
   tapering: spitz zulaufend.
21 **spit-image:** Ebenbild.

"Now what do you make of that?" said Joe Bell, satisfied with my puzzlement.

"It looks like her."

"Listen, boy," and he slapped his hand on the bar, "it *is* her. Sure as I'm a man fit to wear britches. The little Jap knew it was her the minute he saw her."

"He saw her? In Africa?"

"Well. Just the statue there. But it comes to the same thing. Read the facts for yourself," he said, turning over one of the photographs. On the reverse was written: Wood Carving, S Tribe, Tococul, East Anglia, Christmas Day, 1956.

He said, "Here's what the Jap says," and the story was this: On Christmas day Mr. Yunioshi had passed with his camera through Tococul, a village in the tangles of nowhere and of no interest, merely a congregation of mud huts with monkeys in the yards and buzzards on the roofs. He'd decided to move on when he saw suddenly a Negro squatting in a doorway carving monkeys on a walking stick. Mr. Yunioshi was impressed and asked to see more of his work. Whereupon he was shown the carving of the girl's head: and felt, so he told Joe Bell, as

---

2 **puzzlement:** Verwirrung.
4 **to slap:** klatschen, leicht schlagen.
5 **britches:** *breeches* (pl.): Hose.
  Jap (infml.): Japaner, Japs.
8 **to come to s.th.:** auf etwas hinauslaufen.
10 **reverse:** Rückseite.
11 **S Tribe / Tococul / East Anglia:** vermutl. erfundener Stammes- und Ortsname; etwa: südlicher Stamm aus Tococul, East Anglia.
15f. **in the tangles of nowhere** (infml.): irgendwo ganz weit weg im Busch.
16 **congregation:** Ansammlung.
17 **buzzard:** Bussard.
19 **to squat:** hocken.

if he were falling in a dream. But when he offered to buy
it the Negro cupped his private parts in his hand (apparently a tender gesture, comparable to tapping one's
heart) and said no. A pound of salt and ten dollars, a
5 wristwatch and two pounds of salt and twenty dollars,
nothing swayed him. Mr. Yunioshi was in all events
determined to learn how the carving came to be made. It
cost him his salt and his watch, and the incident was
conveyed in African and pig-English and finger-talk.
10 But it would seem that in the spring of that year
a party of three white persons had appeared out of the
brush riding horseback. A young woman and two men.
The men, both red-eyed with fever, were forced for
several weeks to stay shut and shivering in an isolated
15 hut, while the young woman, having presently taken a
fancy to the woodcarver, shared the woodcarver's
mat.

"I don't credit that part," Joe Bell said squeamishly. "I

---

2 **to cup s.th. in one's hand:** die hohle Hand auf etwas legen.
private parts: Geschlechtsteile.
3 **gesture:** Geste, Gebärde.
to tap s.th.: an etwas klopfen, schlagen.
5 **wristwatch:** Armbanduhr.
6 **to sway:** umstimmen.
in all events (pl.): trotz allem.
9 **to convey:** ausdrücken.
pig-English: etwa: Roh-Englisch, gebrochenes Englisch.
finger-talk: Fingersprache.
12 **brush:** Unterholz, Gebüsch.
14 **to stay shut:** eingeschlossen bleiben, im Haus bleiben müssen.
to shiver: zittern, frösteln.
15 f. **to take a fancy to s.o.:** an jdm. Gefallen finden.
16 **woodcarver:** Holzschnitzer.
18 **to credit:** glauben, Glauben schenken.
squeamishly (adv.): empfindlich, zimperlich.

know she had her ways, but I don't think she'd be up to anything as much as that."

"And then?"

"Then nothing," he shrugged. "By and by she went like she come, rode away on a horse."

"Alone, or with the two men?"

Joe Bell blinked. "With the two men, I guess. Now the Jap, he asked about her up and down the country. But nobody else had ever seen her." Then it was as if he could feel my own sense of letdown transmitting itself to him, and he wanted no part of it. "One thing you got to admit, it's the only *definite* news in I don't know how many" – he counted on his fingers: there weren't enough – "years. All I hope, I hope she's rich. She must be rich. You got to be rich to go mucking around in Africa."

"She's probably never set foot in Africa," I said, believing it; yet I could see her there, it was somewhere she would have gone. And the carved head: I looked at the photographs again.

"You know so much, where is she?"

"Dead. Or in a crazy house. Or married. I think she's married and quieted down and maybe right in this very city."

He considered a moment. "No," he said, and shook his

---

1 **to have one's ways** (infml.): so seine Marotten haben.
  to be up to s.th. (infml.): sich auf etwas einlassen, etwas im Sinn haben.
4 **to shrug:** die Achseln zucken.
  by and by: später.
7 **to blink:** blinzeln.
10 **letdown:** Enttäuschung.
  to transmit o.s.: sich übertragen.
15 **to muck around:** herumgammeln.
21 **crazy house** (infml.): Klapsmühle.

head. "I'll tell you why. If she was in this city I'd have seen her. You take a man that likes to walk, a man like me, a man's been walking in the streets going on ten or twelve years, and all those years he's got his eye out for
5 one person, and nobody's ever her, don't it stand to reason she's not there? I see pieces of her all the time, a flat little bottom, any skinny girl that walks fast and straight –" He paused, as though too aware of how intently I was looking at him. "You think I'm round the
10 bend?"

"It's just that I didn't know you'd been in love with her. Not like that."

I was sorry I'd said it; it disconcerted him. He scooped up the photographs and put them back in their envelope. I
15 looked at my watch. I hadn't any place to go, but I thought it was better to leave.

"Hold on," he said, gripping my wrist. "Sure I loved her. But it wasn't that I wanted to touch her." And he added, without smiling: "Not that I don't think about that side of
20 things. Even at my age, and I'll be sixty-seven January ten. It's a peculiar fact – but, the older I grow, that side of things seems to be on my mind more and more. I don't remember thinking about it so much even when I was a youngster and it's every other minute. Maybe the older

---

3 **going on:** hier: jetzt schon fast.
5 **don't** (dial.): *doesn't.*
5 f. **to stand to reason:** logisch sein, zu erwarten sein.
7 **bottom:** Popo, Hintern.
   skinny: dünn.
9 **intently** (adv.): gespannt.
9 f. **round the bend** (infml.): übergeschnappt.
13 **to disconcert:** aus der Fassung bringen.
   to scoop up: an sich raffen.
24 **every other minute:** alle zwei Minuten.

you grow and the less easy it is to put thought into action, maybe that's why it gets all locked up in your head and becomes a burden. Whenever I read in the paper about an old man disgracing himself, I know it's because of this burden. But" – he poured himself a jigger of whiskey and swallowed it neat – "I'll never disgrace myself. And I swear, it never crossed my mind about Holly. You can love somebody without it being like that. You keep them a stranger, a stranger who's a friend."

Two men came into the bar, and it seemed the moment to leave. Joe Bell followed me to the door. He caught my wrist again. "Do you believe it?"

"That you didn't want to touch her?"

"I mean about Africa."

At that moment I couldn't seem to remember the story, only the image of her riding away on a horse. "Anyway, she's gone."

"Yeah," he said, opening the door. "Just gone."

Outside, the rain had stopped, there was only a mist of it in the air, so I turned the corner and walked along the street where the brownstone stands. It is a street with trees that in the summer make cool patterns on the pavement; but now the leaves were yellowed and mostly down, and the rain had made them slippery, they skidded underfoot. The brownstone is midway in the block, next to a church where a blue tower-clock tolls the hours. It

---

4 **to disgrace o.s.:** sich schlecht benehmen.
5 **jigger:** Maßeinheit für alkoholische Getränke (1,5 Unzen, etwa 42 cm³); ‚Doppelter'.
6 **neat:** pur (Alkohol).
22 f. **pavement:** Bürgersteig.
24 **to skid:** rutschen.
26 **to toll:** schlagen (Uhren, Glocken).

12

has been sleeked up since my day; a smart black door has replaced the old frosted glass, and gray elegant shutters frame the windows. No one I remember still lives there except Madame Sapphia Spanella, a husky coloratura[7] who every afternoon went roller-skating in Central Park[8]. I know she's still there because I went up the steps and looked at the mailboxes. It was one of these mailboxes that had first made me aware of Holly Golightly.

*

I'd been living in the house about a week when I noticed that the mailbox belonging to Apt. 2 had a name-slot fitted with a curious card. Printed, rather Cartier-formal[9], it read: *Miss Holiday Golightly*; and, underneath, in the corner, *Traveling*. It nagged me like a tune: *Miss Holiday Golightly, Traveling.*

One night, it was long past twelve, I woke up at the sound of Mr. Yunioshi calling down the stairs. Since he lived on the top floor, his voice fell through the whole house, exasperated and stern. "Miss Golightly! I must protest!"

The voice that came back, welling up from the bottom of

---

1 **to sleek up:** auf Hochglanz bringen.
  smart: elegant.
2 **frosted glass:** Milchglas.
  shutter: Blendladen.
4 **husky:** heiser.
  coloratura: Koloratursopranistin (s. Anm.).
5 **roller-skating:** Rollschuhlaufen.
10 **name-slot:** Schlitz für Namensschild.
11 f. **Cartier-formal:** nach Cartier-Art (s. Anm.).
12 **underneath:** darunter.
13 **to nag:** keine Ruhe lassen.
18 **exasperated:** gereizt.
20 **to well up:** hochsteigen.

the stairs, was silly-young and self-amused. "Oh, darling, I *am* sorry. I lost the goddamn key."

"You cannot go on ringing my bell. You must please, please have yourself a key made."

5 "But I lose them all."

"I work, I have to sleep," Mr. Yunioshi shouted. "But always you are ringing my bell ..."

"Oh, *don't* be angry, you *dear* little man: I *won't* do it again. And if you promise not to be angry" – her voice
10 was coming nearer, she was climbing the stairs – "I might let you take those pictures we mentioned."

By now I'd left my bed and opened the door an inch. I could hear Mr. Yunioshi's silence: hear, because it was accompanied by an audible change of breath.

15 "When?" he said.

The girl laughed. "Sometime," she answered, slurring the word.

"Any time," he said, and closed his door.

I went out into the hall and leaned over the banister, just
20 enough to see without being seen. She was still on the stairs, now she reached the landing, and the ragbag colors of her boy's hair, tawny streaks, strands of albino-blond and yellow, caught the hall light. It was a warm

---

1 **self-amused:** etwa: über sich selbst belustigt, albern.
2 **goddamn** (infml.): gottverdammt (von *goddamned*).
14 **audible:** hörbar.
16 **to slur:** undeutlich sprechen, halb verschlucken.
19 **banister:** Treppengeländer.
21 **landing:** Treppenabsatz.
   ragbag: wild gemischt.
22 **tawny:** gelbbraun.
   streak: Streifen, Strähne.
   strand: Strähne.
22 f. **albino-blond:** albinoblond, weißblond.

14

evening, nearly summer, and she wore a slim cool black
dress, black sandals, a pearl choker. For all her chic thinness, she had an almost breakfast-cereal air of health, a
soap and lemon cleanness, a rough pink darkening in the
5 cheeks. Her mouth was large, her nose upturned. A pair
of dark glasses blotted out her eyes. It was a face beyond
childhood, yet this side of belonging to a woman. I
thought her anywhere between sixteen and thirty; as it
turned out, she was shy two months of her nineteenth
10 birthday.
She was not alone. There was a man following behind
her. The way his plump hand clutched at her hip seemed
somehow improper; not morally, aesthetically. He was
short and vast, sun-lamped and pomaded, a man in a
15 buttressed pin-stripe suit with a red carnation withering

---

1 **slim:** dünn.
1 f. **cool dress:** Sommerkleid (*cool:* auch [infml.]: stark, klasse).
2 **choker:** enger Halsreif.
3 **breakfast-cereal:** Frühstücksgetreideflocken, Müsli.
   air: Aussehen, Anschein.
5 **her nose** (*was*) **upturned:** sie hatte eine Stupsnase.
6 **to blot out:** verdecken.
7 **this side of** (infml.): noch nicht ganz.
9 **shy** (AE, infml.): kaum.
12 **plump:** dicklich.
   to clutch: packen.
   hip: Hüfte.
13 **improper:** unziemlich, unangemessen.
14 **vast:** umfänglich.
   sun-lamped: von der Höhensonne gebräunt.
   pomaded: mit Pomade in den Haaren.
15 **buttressed:** verstärkt; hier etwa: steif.
   pin-stripe: Nadelstreifen.
   carnation: Nelke (Blume).
   to wither: welken.

in the lapel. When they reached her door she rummaged
her purse in search of a key, and took no notice of the fact
that his thick lips were nuzzling the nape of her neck. At
last, though, finding the key and opening her door, she
5 turned to him cordially: "Bless you, darling – you were
sweet to see me home."

"Hey, baby!" he said, for the door was closing in his
face.

"Yes, Harry?"

10 "Harry was the other guy. I'm Sid. Sid Arbuck. You like
me."

"I worship you, Mr. Arbuck. But good night, Mr. Arbuck."

Mr. Arbuck stared with disbelief as the door shut firmly.

15 "Hey, baby, let me in, baby. You like me, baby. I'm a
liked guy. Didn't I pick up the check, five people, *your*
friends, I never seen them before? Don't that give me the
right you should like me? You like me, baby."

He tapped on the door gently, then louder; finally he took

20 several steps back, his body hunched and lowering, as
though he meant to charge it, crash it down. Instead, he
plunged down the stairs, slamming a fist against the wall.

---

1 **lapel:** (Jackett-)Aufschlag, Revers.
   to rummage: durchwühlen.
3 **to nuzzle:** beschnüffeln, beschnuppern.
   nape of one's neck: Nacken.
5 **cordially** (adv.): herzlich.
10 **guy** (infml.): Typ, Bursche, Knabe.
16 **to pick up the check:** die Rechnung übernehmen, zahlen (*check:*
   Restaurantrechnung [AE]).
20 **hunched:** zusammengekauert.
   lowering: finster drohend.
22 **to plunge down:** hinunterstürzen, herabpoltern.
   to slam: schlagen, knallen.

16

Just as he reached the bottom, the door of the girl's apartment opened and she poked out her head.

"Oh, Mr. *Ar*buck ..."

He turned back, a smile of relief oiling his face: she'd only been teasing.

"The next time a girl wants a little powder-room change," she called, not teasing at all, "take my advice, darling: *don't* give her twenty-cents!"

*

She kept her promise to Mr. Yunioshi; or I assume she did not ring his bell again, for in the next days she started ringing mine, sometimes at two in the morning, three and four: she had no qualms at what hour she got me out of bed to push the buzzer that released the downstairs door. As I had few friends, and none who would come around so late, I always knew that it was her. But on the first occasions of its happening, I went to my door, half-expecting bad news, a telegram; and Miss Golightly would call up: "Sorry, darling – I forgot my key."

Of course we'd never met. Though actually, on the stairs, in the street, we often came face-to-face; but she seemed not quite to see me. She was never without dark glasses, she was always well groomed, there was a consequential good taste in the plainness of her clothes, the blues and

---

2 **to poke out:** herausstrecken.
5 **to tease:** necken, hänseln.
6 **powder-room:** Damentoilette.
12 **qualm:** Gewissensbiß.
13 **buzzer:** Summer; hier: (Tür-)Drücker.
23 **well groomed:** gepflegt.
   consequential: hier: konsequent, folgerichtig.

17

grays and lack of luster that made her, herself, shine so. One might have thought her a photographer's model, perhaps a young actress, except that it was obvious, judging from her hours, she hadn't time to be either.

Now and then I ran across her outside our neighborhood. Once a visiting relative took me to "21"[10], and there, at a superior table, surrounded by four men, none of them Mr. Arbuck, yet all of them interchangeable with him, was Miss Golightly, idly, publicly combing her hair; and her expression, an unrealized yawn, put, by example, a dampener on the excitement I felt over dining at so swanky a place. Another night, deep in the summer, the heat of my room sent me out into the streets. I walked down Third Avenue to Fifty-first Street[11], where there was an antique store with an object in its window I admired: a palace of a bird cage, a mosque of minarets and bamboo rooms yearning to be filled with talkative parrots. But the price was three hundred and fifty dollars. On the way home I noticed a cab-driver crowd gathered in front of P. J. Clark's saloon[12], apparently

---

1 **luster:** Glanz.
4 **hours:** hier: Zeiten (zu denen jd. nach Hause kommt).
6 **relative:** Verwandte(r).
8 **interchangeable:** austauschbar.
10 **unrealized:** hier: nicht ausgeführt, unterdrückt.
11 **dampener:** Dämpfer.
12 **swanky** (infml.): nobel, piekfein, protzig.
15 **antique store:** Antiquitätengeschäft.
16 **mosque:** Moschee.
17 **bamboo:** Bambus.
   to yearn: (nach etwas) verlangen.
   talkative: geschwätzig.
18 **parrot:** Papagei.
19 **cab-driver:** Taxifahrer.

attracted there by a happy group of whiskey-eyed Australian army officers baritoning, "Waltzing Matilda[13]."
As they sang they took turns spin-dancing a girl over the cobbles under the El; and the girl, Miss Golightly, to be sure, floated round in their arms light as a scarf.

But if Miss Golightly remained unconscious of my existence, except as a doorbell convenience, I became, through the summer, rather an authority on hers. I discovered, from observing the trash-basket outside her door, that her regular reading consisted of tabloids and travel folders and astrological charts; that she smoked an esoteric cigarette called Picayunes[14]; survived on cottage cheese and melba toast; that her vari-colored hair was somewhat self-induced. The same source made it evident that she received V-letters by the bale. They were always torn into strips like bookmarks. I used occasionally to

---

2 **to baritone:** im Bariton singen.
3 **to take turns doing s.th.:** etwas abwechselnd tun.
  to spin-dance s.o.: mit jdm. im Kreis herumtanzen, jdn. im Kreis herumwirbeln.
4 **cobble:** Pflasterstein.
  El: Abk. für *Elevated railroad:* Hochbahn (*elevated:* erhöht, hoch).
5 **scarf:** Schal.
7 **convenience:** Annehmlichkeit.
8 **authority:** Kenner.
9 **trash-basket** (AE): Papierkorb.
10 **tabloid:** Boulevardzeitung.
11 **travel folder:** Reisebroschüre.
  astrological charts: astrologische Tabellen, astrologische Diagramme.
13 **melba toast:** dünner Toast.
  vari-colored: verschiedenfarbig.
14 **self-induced:** selbstverursacht (d. h. Hollys Haarfarbe ist nicht natürlich).
15 **V-letter:** etwa: Sieg-Brief.
  bale: Bündel.

pluck myself a bookmark in passing. *Remember* and *miss you* and *rain* and *please write* and *damn* and *goddamn* were the words that recurred most often on these slips; those, and *lonesome* and *love.*

5 Also, she had a cat and she played the guitar. On days when the sun was strong, she would wash her hair, and together with the cat, a red tiger-striped tom, sit out on the fire escape thumbing a guitar while her hair dried. Whenever I heard the music, I would go stand quietly by
10 my window. She played very well, and sometimes sang too. Sang in the hoarse, breaking tones of a boy's adolescent voice. She knew all the show hits, Cole Porter and Kurt Weill;[15] especially she liked the songs from *Oklahoma!*[16], which were new that summer and every-
15 where. But there were moments when she played songs that made you wonder where she learned them, where indeed she came from. Harsh-tender wandering tunes with words that smacked of pineywoods or prairie. One went: *Don't wanna sleep, Don't wanna die, Just wanna go*
20 *a-travelin' through the pastures of the sky;* and this one seemed to gratify her the most, for often she continued it

---

3 **to recur:** sich wiederholen.
7 **tom:** Kurzform von *tomcat:* Kater.
8 **to thumb:** hier: (die Saiten eines Instruments) mit dem Daumen zupfen.
11 **hoarse:** rauh.
11 f. **adolescent:** heranwachsend, in der Pubertät.
17 **harsh-tender:** herb-zart, rauh-zärtlich.
   wandering: unstet, umherschweifend.
18 **to smack of s.th.:** nach etwas schmecken.
   pineywood: Kiefernwald.
   prairie: Prärie, Grassteppe.
19 **wanna** (dial.): *want to.*
21 **to gratify:** erfreuen, befriedigen.

20

long after her hair had dried, after the sun had gone and there were lighted windows in the dusk.

But our acquaintance did not make headway until September, an evening with the first ripple-chills of autumn running through it. I'd been to a movie, come home and gone to bed with a bourbon nightcap and the newest Simenon[17]: so much my idea of comfort that I couldn't understand a sense of unease that multiplied until I could hear my heart beating. It was a feeling I'd read about, written about, but never before experienced. The feeling of being watched. Of someone in the room. Then: an abrupt rapping at the window, a glimpse of ghostly gray: I spilled the bourbon. It was some little while before I could bring myself to open the window, and ask Miss Golightly what she wanted.

"I've got the most terrifying man downstairs," she said, stepping off the fire escape into the room. "I mean he's sweet when he isn't drunk, but let him start lapping up the vino, and oh God quel beast! If there's one thing I loathe, it's men who bite." She loosened a gray flannel robe off her shoulder to show me evidence of what hap-

---

3 **to make headway:** Fortschritte machen.
4 **ripple-chill:** etwa: kühler, das Wasser kräuselnder Wind.
6 **nightcap:** Schlaftrunk.
8 **unease:** Unbehagen.
12 **to rap:** klopfen.
   ghostly: geisterhaft.
13 **to spill:** verschütten.
16 **terrifying:** fürchterlich.
18 f. **to lap up the vino** (infml.): sich den Wein reinschlabbern.
19 **quel** (Fr.): was für ein.
20 **to loathe:** verabscheuen, nicht ausstehen können.
   to loosen: lösen, ablegen.
   flannel: Flanell.
21 **robe:** Hauskleid, Morgenmantel (AE).

pens if a man bites. The robe was all she was wearing.
"I'm sorry if I frightened you. But when the beast got so
tiresome I just went out the window. I think he thinks I'm
in the bathroom, not that I give a damn what he thinks,
the hell with him, he'll get tired, he'll go to sleep, my God
he should, eight martinis before dinner and enough wine
to wash an elephant. Listen, you can throw me out if you
want to. I've got a gall barging in on you like this. But
that fire escape was damned icy. And you looked so cozy.
Like my brother Fred. We used to sleep four in a bed,
and he was the only one that ever let me hug him on a
cold night. By the way, do you mind if I call you Fred?"
She'd come completely into the room now, and she
paused there, staring at me. I'd never seen her before not
wearing dark glasses, and it was obvious now that they
were prescription lenses, for without them her eyes had
an assessing squint, like a jeweler's. They were large
eyes, a little blue, a little green, dotted with bits of
brown: vari-colored, like her hair; and, like her hair,
they gave out a lively warm light. "I suppose you think
I'm very brazen. Or *très fou*. Or something."

---

3 **tiresome:** lästig.
4 **not to give a damn:** sich den Teufel (um etwas) scheren.
8 **gall:** Unverschämtheit.
  to barge in: hereinplatzen.
9 **cozy:** behaglich, gemütlich.
11 **to hug:** umarmen.
16 **prescription lenses** (pl.): (vom Arzt verschriebene) Brille (*lens:* Brillenglas).
17 **assessing:** taxierend.
  squint: Schielen, (argwöhnischer) Seitenblick.
18 **dotted:** gesprenkelt.
21 **brazen:** dreist.
  très fou (Fr.): ganz verrückt.

22

"Not at all."

She seemed disappointed. "Yes, you do. Everybody does. I don't mind. It's useful."

She sat down on one of the rickety red-velvet chairs, curved her legs underneath her, and glanced round the room, her eyes puckering more pronouncedly. "How can you bear it? It's a chamber of horrors."

"Oh, you get used to anything," I said, annoyed with myself, for actually I was proud of the place.

"I don't. I'll never get used to anything. Anybody that does, they might as well be dead." Her dispraising eyes surveyed the room again. "What do you *do* here all day?"

I motioned toward a table tall with books and paper. "Write things."

"I thought writers were quite old. Of course Saroyan[18] isn't old. I met him at a party, and really he isn't old at all. In fact," she mused, "if he'd give himself a closer shave ... by the way, is Hemingway[19] old?"

"In his forties, I should think."

"That's not bad. I can't get excited by a man until he's forty-two. I know this idiot girl who keeps telling me I ought to go to a head-shrinker; she says I have a father complex. Which is so much *merde*. I simply *trained* myself to like older men, and it was the smartest thing I ever did. How old is W. Somerset Maugham[20]?"

---

4 **rickety:** wackelig.
6 **to pucker:** sich zusammenziehen, kleiner machen.
   pronouncedly (adv.): ausgeprägt, deutlich.
11 **dispraising:** mißbilligend.
18 **to muse:** nachdenken.
23 **head-shrinker** (slang): Seelenmasseur, Psychiater.
24 **merde** (Fr.): Scheiße.
25 **smart:** schlau.

"I'm not sure. Sixty-something."

"That's not bad. I've never been to bed with a writer. No, wait: do you know Benny Shacklett?" She frowned when I shook my head. "That's funny. He's written an awful lot of radio stuff. But quel rat. Tell me, are you a real writer?"

"It depends on what you mean by real."

"Well, darling, does anyone *buy* what you write?"

"Not yet."

"I'm going to help you," she said. "I can, too. Think of all the people I know who know people. I'm going to help you because you look like my brother Fred. Only smaller. I haven't seen him since I was fourteen, that's when I left home, and he was already six-feet-two. My other brothers were more your size, runts. It was the peanut butter that made Fred so tall. Everybody thought it was dotty, the way he gorged himself on peanut butter; he didn't care about anything in this world except horses and peanut butter. But he wasn't dotty, just sweet and vague and terribly slow; he'd been in the eighth grade three years when I ran away. Poor Fred. I wonder if the Army's generous with their peanut butter. Which reminds me, I'm starving."

I pointed to a bowl of apples, at the same time asked her how and why she'd left home so young. She looked at me blankly, and rubbed her nose, as though it tickled: a gesture, seeing often repeated, I came to recognize as a

---

15 **runt** (pej.): Zwerg, Wicht.

15f. **peanut butter:** Erdnußbutter.

17 **dotty** (infml.): verrückt.

    to gorge o.s. on s.th.: etwas in sich hineinschlingen.

26 **blankly** (adv.): verständnislos, ausdruckslos.

    to tickle: kitzeln.

signal that one was trespassing. Like many people with a bold fondness for volunteering intimate information, anything that suggested a direct question, a pinning-down, put her on guard. She took a bite of apple, and said: "Tell me something you've written. The story part."

"That's one of the troubles. They're not the kind of stories you *can* tell."

"Too dirty?"

"Maybe I'll let you read one sometime."

"Whiskey and apples go together. Fix me a drink, darling. Then you can read me a story yourself."

Very few authors, especially the unpublished, can resist an invitation to read aloud. I made us both a drink and, settling in a chair opposite, began to read to her, my voice a little shaky with a combination of stage fright and enthusiasm: it was a new story, I'd finished it the day before, and that inevitable sense of shortcoming had not had time to develop. It was about two women who share a house, schoolteachers, one of whom, when the other becomes engaged, spreads with anonymous notes a scandal that prevents the marriage. As I read, each glimpse I stole of Holly made my heart contract. She fidgeted. She

---

1 **to trespass:** (fig.) die Grenze überschreiten, sich vergehen.
2 **fondness:** Vorliebe, Faible.
  to volunteer: hier: ungefragt mitteilen.
3 f. **to pin down:** festnageln.
11 **to fix:** (alkoholisches Getränk) machen, mischen (AE).
16 **shaky:** zittrig.
  stage fright: Lampenfieber.
18 **inevitable:** unvermeidlich.
  shortcoming: Mangel, Fehler, Scheitern, Fehlschlag.
21 **engaged:** verlobt.
23 **to contract:** sich zusammenziehen.
  to fidget: zappeln, unruhig hin und her rutschen.

picked apart the butts in an ash-tray, she mooned over
her fingernails, as though longing for a file; worse, when
I did seem to have her interest, there was actually a telltale frost over her eyes, as if she were wondering whether
to buy a pair of shoes she'd seen in some window.
"Is that the *end?*" she asked, waking up. She floundered
for something more to say. "Of course I like dykes them-
selves. They don't scare me a bit. But stories about dykes
bore the bejesus out of me. I just can't put myself in their
shoes. Well really, darling," she said, because I was
clearly puzzled, "if it's not about a couple of old bull-
dykes, what the hell *is* it about?"
But I was in no mood to compound the mistake of having
read the story with the further embarrassment of explain-
ing it. The same vanity that had led to such exposure,
now forced me to mark her down as an insensitive, mind-
less show-off.

1 **butt** (AE, slang): (Zigaretten-)Kippe.
 ash-tray: Aschenbecher.
  to moon over s.th.: verträumt auf etwas schauen.
2 **file:** Feile.
3f. **telltale:** verräterisch, Bände sprechend.
4 **frost:** hier (fig.): Frost, Frostigkeit, Eisigkeit.
6 **to flounder:** sich verzweifelt bemühen.
7 **dyke** (slang): Lesbe.
9 **to bore the bejesus out of s.o.:** etwa: jdn. zu Tode langweilen (*bejesus:
 by Jesus*).
11f. **bull-dyke** (slang): ‚kesser Vater‘, Lesbierin mit maskulinen Nei-
 gungen.
13 **to compound:** verschlimmern.
14 **embarrassment:** Peinlichkeit.
15 **exposure:** Bloßstellung, Entlarvung.
16 **to mark down:** im Preis herabsetzen.
  insensitive: gefühllos.
17 **show-off:** Angeber(in).

"Incidentally," she said, "do you happen to *know* any nice lesbians? I'm looking for a roommate. Well, don't laugh. I'm so disorganized, I simply can't afford a maid; and really, dykes are wonderful homemakers, they love
5 to do all the work, you never have to bother about brooms and defrosting and sending out the laundry. I had a roommate in Hollywood, she played in Westerns, they called her the Lone Ranger; but I'll say this for her, she was better than a man around the house. Of course peo-
10 ple couldn't help but think I must be a bit of a dyke myself. And of course I am. Everyone is: a bit. So what? That never discouraged a man yet, in fact it seems to goad them on. Look at the Lone Ranger, married twice. Usually dykes only get married once, just for the name.
15 It seems to carry such cachet later on to be called Mrs. Something Another. That's not true!" She was staring at an alarm clock on the table. "It can't be four-thirty!" The window was turning blue. A sunrise breeze bandied the curtains.
20 "What is today?"
"Thursday."
"Thursday." She stood up. "My God," she said, and sat down again with a moan. "It's too gruesome."

---

1 **incidentally** (adv.): übrigens.
2 **roommate:** Zimmergenosse, -genossin.
4 **homemaker** (AE): Hausmutter.
5 **to bother about s.th.:** sich mit etwas plagen.
6 **to defrost:** enteisen.
   laundry: Wäsche.
8 **lone ranger:** etwa: Einzelkämpfer, einsamer Förster, einsamer Jäger.
13 **to goad on:** (fig.) anstacheln.
15 **cachet:** Gütesiegel.
18 **to bandy:** hin und her flattern (lassen).
23 **gruesome:** schaurig, schauerlich.

I was tired enough not to be curious. I lay down on the
bed and closed my eyes. Still it was irresistible: "What's
gruesome about Thursday?"

"Nothing. Except that I can never remember when it's
coming. You see, on Thursdays I have to catch the eight
forty-five. They're so particular about visiting hours, so if
you're there by ten that gives you an hour before the poor
men eat lunch. Think of it, lunch at eleven. You *can* go at
two, and I'd so much rather, but he likes me to come in
the morning, he says it sets him up for the rest of the day.
I've *got* to stay awake," she said, pinching her cheeks
until the roses came, "there isn't time to sleep, I'd look
consumptive, I'd sag like a tenement, and that wouldn't
be fair: a girl can't go to Sing Sing[21] with a green face."

"I suppose not." The anger I felt at her over my story was
ebbing; she absorbed me again.

"All the visitors *do* make an effort to look their best, and
it's very tender, it's sweet as hell, the way the women
wear their prettiest everything, I mean the old ones and
the really poor ones too, they make the dearest effort to
look nice and smell nice too, and I love them for it. I love
the kids too, especially the colored ones. I mean the kids
the wives bring. It should be sad, seeing the kids there,
but it isn't, they have ribbons in their hair and lots of
shine on their shoes, you'd think there was going to be ice

---

2 **irresistible:** unwiderstehlich.
6 **particular:** eigen, pingelig.
11 **to pinch:** kneifen.
12 **until the roses came:** bis (wieder) Farbe ins Gesicht kam.
13 **consumptive:** schwindsüchtig.
    to sag like a tenement (infml.): wie eine Mietskaserne (bei der Spren-
    gung) zusammensacken.
16 **to ebb:** verebben, abnehmen.
22 **kid:** Kind.

28

cream; and sometimes that's what it's like in the visitors' room, a party. Anyway it's not like the movies: you know, grim whisperings through a grille. There isn't any grille, just a counter between you and them, and the kids
5 can stand on it to be hugged; all you have to do to kiss somebody is lean across. What I like most, they're so happy to see each other, they've saved up so much to talk about, it isn't possible to be dull, they keep laughing and holding hands. It's different afterwards," she said. "I see
10 them on the train. They sit so quiet watching the river go by." She stretched a strand of hair to the corner of her mouth and nibbled it thoughtfully. "I'm keeping you awake. Go to sleep."

"Please. I'm interested."

15 "I know you are. That's why I want you to go to sleep. Because if I keep on, I'll tell you about Sally. I'm not sure that would be quite cricket." She chewed her hair silently. "They never *told* me not to tell anyone. In so many words. And it *is* funny. Maybe you could put it in a
20 story with different names and whatnot. Listen, Fred," she said, reaching for another apple, "you've got to cross your heart and kiss your elbow –"

Perhaps contortionists can kiss their elbow; she had to accept an approximation.

---

3 **grille:** Sprechgitter.
4 **counter:** Theke, Tisch.
12 **to nibble s.th.:** an etwas knabbern, kauen.
17 **cricket** (fig., infml.): (sportlich) fair.
   to chew: kauen.
18 f. **in so many words:** ausdrücklich.
21 f. **to cross one's heart:** ein Kreuz über dem Herzen schlagen (um ein Versprechen zu besiegeln).
23 **contortionist:** Schlangenmensch.
24 **approximation:** Näherung, Annäherung.

"Well," she said, with a mouthful of apple, "you may have read about him in the papers. His name is Sally Tomato, and I speak Yiddish[22] better than he speaks English; but he's a darling old man, terribly pious.
5 He'd look like a monk if it weren't for the gold teeth; he says he prays for me every night. Of course he was never my lover; as far as that goes, I never knew him until he was already in jail. But I adore him now, after all I've been going to see him every Thursday for seven
10 months, and I think I'd go even if he didn't pay me. This one's mushy," she said, and aimed the rest of the apple out the window. "By the way, I *did* know Sally by sight. He used to come to Joe Bell's bar, the one around the corner: never talked to anybody, just stand
15 there, like the kind of man who lives in hotel rooms. But it's funny to remember back and realize how closely he must have been watching me, because right after they sent him up (Joe Bell showed me his picture in the paper. Blackhand. Mafia.[23] All that mumbo
20 jumbo: but they gave him five years) along came this telegram from a lawyer. It said to contact him immediately for information to my advantage."

"You thought somebody had left you a million?"

"Not at all. I figured Bergdorf was trying to collect. But I

---

3 **Yiddish:** Jiddisch (dem Deutschen verwandte, jüdische Sprache) (s. Anm.).
5 **monk:** Mönch.
8 **jail:** Gefängnis.
   to adore: anbeten.
11 **mushy:** matschig.
19 **Blackhand:** wörtl.: Schwarze Hand (italo-amerikanische Gangster-organisation).
19 f. **mumbo jumbo:** Mumpitz, Hokuspokus.
24 **to figure:** denken, meinen (AE).

took the gamble and went to see this lawyer (if he *is* a
lawyer, which I doubt, since he doesn't seem to have an
office, just an answering service, and he always wants to
meet you in Hamburg Heaven[24]: that's because he's fat,
5 he can eat ten hamburgers and two bowls of relish and a
whole lemon meringue pie). He asked me how I'd like to
cheer up a lonely old man, at the same time pick up a
hundred a week. I told him look, darling, you've got the
wrong Miss Golightly, I'm not a nurse that does tricks on
10 the side. I wasn't impressed by the honorarium either;
you can do as well as that on trips to the powder room:
any gent with the slightest chic will give you fifty for the
girl's john, and I always ask for cab fare too, that's
another fifty. But then he told me his client was Sally
15 Tomato. He said dear old Sally had long admired me *à la
distance*, so wouldn't it be a good deed if I went to visit
him once a week. Well, I couldn't say no: it was too romantic."

"I don't know. It doesn't sound right."
20 She smiled. "You think I'm lying?"

"For one thing, they can't simply let *any*one visit a pris-
oner."

"Oh, they don't. In fact they make quite a boring fuss.
I'm supposed to be his niece."

1 **gamble:** Risiko, Wagnis.
3 **answering service:** Anrufbeantworter.
5 **relish:** gewürzte Sauce (Remoulade o. ä.); Vorspeise.
6 **meringue pie:** Baisertorte.
9f. **to do tricks on the side** (slang): sich nebenher (mit ‚Nummern')
etwas verdienen.
12 **gent:** Kurzform von *gentleman*.
13 **girls' john** (infml.): Damenklo.
15f. **à la distance** (Fr.): aus der Ferne.
23 **to make a fuss:** Theater machen.

"And it's as simple as that? For an hour's conversation he gives you a hundred dollars?"

"He doesn't, the lawyer does. Mr. O'Shaughnessy mails it to me in cash as soon as I leave the weather report."

5 "I think you could get into a lot of trouble," I said, and switched off a lamp; there was no need of it now, morning was in the room and pigeons were gargling on the fire escape.

"How?" she said seriously.

10 "There must be something in the law books about false identity. After all, you're *not* his niece. And what about this weather report?"

She patted a yawn. "But it's nothing. Just messages I leave with the answering service so Mr. O'Shaughnessy

15 will know for sure that I've been up there. Sally tells me what to say, things like, oh, 'there's a hurricane in Cuba' and 'it's snowing in Palermo.' Don't worry, darling," she said, moving to the bed, "I've taken care of myself a long time." The morning light seemed refracted through her:

20 as she pulled the bed covers up to my chin she gleamed like a transparent child; then she lay down beside me. "Do you mind? I only want to rest a moment. So let's don't say another word. Go to sleep."

I pretended to, I made my breathing heavy and regular.

25 Bells in the tower of the next-door church rang the half-

---

3 **to mail:** per Post schicken.
7 **to gargle:** gurren.
13 **to pat a yawn:** sich leicht auf den Mund schlagen, um ein Gähnen zu verbergen.
16 **hurricane:** Hurrikan (Wirbelsturm in Mittelamerika).
19 **refracted:** gebrochen (Licht).
21 **transparent:** durchsichtig.
22 f. **let's don't** (infml.): *don't let's*.

32

hour, the hour. It was six when she put her hand on my
arm, a fragile touch careful not to waken. "Poor Fred,"
she whispered, and it seemed she was speaking to me,
but she was not. "Where are you, Fred? Because it's
cold. There's snow in the wind." Her cheek came to rest
against my shoulder, a warm damp weight.
"Why are you crying?"
She sprang back, sat up. "Oh, for God's sake," she said,
starting for the window and the fire escape, "I *hate*
snoops."

*

The next day, Friday, I came home to find outside my
door a grand-luxe Charles & Co.[25] basket with her card:
Miss Holiday Golightly, Traveling: and scribbled on the
back in a freakishly awkward, kindergarten hand: *Bless*
you darling Fred. Please forgive the other night. You were
an angel about the whole thing. Mille tendresse – Holly.
P. S. I won't bother you again. I replied, *Please do*, and
left this note at her door with what I could afford, a bunch
of street-vendor violets. But apparently she'd meant
what she said; I neither saw nor heard from her, and I
gathered she'd gone so far as to obtain a downstairs key.
At any rate she no longer rang my bell. I missed that; and

---

2 **fragile:** hier: leicht, zart.
10 **snoop:** Schnüffler.
12 **grand-luxe** (Fr.): etwa: superluxus.
13 **to scribble:** kritzeln.
14 **freakishly** (adv.): verrückt, irre.
   awkward: unbeholfen.
16 **mille tendresse** (Fr.): richtig: *mille tendresses:* etwa: tausend Küsse.
19 **street-vendor:** Straßenhändler, -verkäufer.
   violet: Veilchen.

as the days merged I began to feel toward her certain far-fetched resentments, as if I were being neglected by my closest friend. A disquieting loneliness came into my life, but it induced no hunger for friends of longer
5 acquaintance: they seemed now like a salt-free, sugar-less diet. By Wednesday thoughts of Holly, of Sing Sing and Sally Tomato, of worlds where men forked over fifty dollars for the powder room, were so constant that I couldn't work. That night I left a message
10 in her mailbox: *Tomorrow is Thursday*. The next morning rewarded me with a second note in the play-pen script: *Bless you for reminding me. Can you stop for a drink tonight 6-ish?*
I waited until ten past six, then made myself delay five
15 minutes more.
A creature answered the door. He smelled of cigars and Knize cologne. His shoes sported elevated heels; without these added inches, one might have taken him for a Little Person. His bald freckled head was dwarf-big: attached

---

1 **to merge:** ineinander übergehen.
2 **far-fetched:** weit hergeholt.
  resentment: Ärger, Groll, Unwille.
3 **disquieting:** beunruhigend.
4 **to induce s.th.:** zu etwas führen.
7f. **to fork over:** (Geld) locker machen.
11 **play-pen:** Laufstall; hier: Kleinkinder-.
12 **script:** Schrift.
13 **6-ish:** (infml.): so um sechs Uhr herum.
17 **Knize cologne:** Eau de Cologne, Kölnisch Wasser der Marke Knize (berühmter Herrenausstatter in der East 56th St.).
  to sport: (stolz) vorweisen.
18f. **Little Person:** hier: Kobold, Gnom.
19 **bald:** kahl, glatzköpfig.
  dwarf-big: zwergenhaft dick.
19f. **attached to s.th.:** zu etwas gehörig.

34

to it were a pair of pointed, truly elfin ears. He had
Pekingese eyes, unpitying and slightly bulged. Tufts of
hair sprouted from his ears, from his nose; his jowls were
gray with afternoon beard, and his handshake almost
5 furry.

"Kid's in the shower," he said, motioning a cigar toward
a sound of water hissing in another room. The room in
which we stood (we were standing because there was
nothing to sit on) seemed as though it were being just
10 moved into; you expected to smell wet paint. Suitcases
and unpacked crates were the only furniture. The crates
served as tables. One supported the mixings of a martini;
another a lamp, a Libertyphone, Holly's red cat and a
bowl of yellow roses. Bookcases, covering one wall,
15 boasted a half-shelf of literature. I warmed to the room at
once, I liked its fly-by-night look.

The man cleared his throat. "You expected?"

He found my nod uncertain. His cold eyes operated on

---

1 **elfin:** koboldähnlich.
2 **Pekingese:** pekinesenhaft, wie ein Pekinese.
  bulged: vorstehend.
  tuft: Büschel.
3 **to sprout:** sprießen, wachsen.
  jowl: Backe.
5 **furry:** pelzig.
7 **to hiss:** zischen.
10 **suitcase:** Koffer.
11 **crate:** Kiste.
12 **mixing:** hier: Zutat zum Mischen von Getränken.
13 **Libertyphone:** Telefon aus dem Warenangebot der Kaufhauskette
  Liberty.
14 **bookcase:** Bücherschrank.
15 **a half-shelf:** ein halbes Fach voll.
  to warm to s.th.: sich für etwas erwärmen.
16 **fly-by-night** (fig.): leichtsinnig, wie ein Windhund.
18 **to operate on s.o.:** hier (fig.): jdn. sezieren.

me, made neat, exploratory incisions. "A lot of characters come here, they're not expected. You know the kid long?"

"Not very."

5 "So you don't know the kid long?"

"I live upstairs."

The answer seemed to explain enough to relax him. "You got the same layout?"

"Much smaller."

10 He tapped ash on the floor. "This is a dump. This is unbelievable. But the kid don't know how to live even when she's got the dough." His speech had a jerky metallic rhythm, like a teletype. "So," he said, "what do you think: is she or ain't she?"

15 "Ain't she what?"

"A phony."

"I wouldn't have thought so."

"You're wrong. She is a phony. But on the other hand you're right. She isn't a phony because she's a *real* phony.

20 She believes all this crap she believes. You can't talk her out of it. I've tried with tears running down my cheeks. Benny Polan, respected everywhere, Benny Polan tried.

---

1 **exploratory:** Explorations-, untersuchend, erforschend.
  incision: Schnitt, Einschnitt.
7 **to relax:** entspannen.
8 **layout:** Anordnung, Anlage.
10 **dump:** Müllkippe.
11 **even:** ruhig, in Ruhe.
12 **dough** (infml.): ‚Knete‘, Geld.
  jerky: stoßartig.
13 **teletype:** Kurzform von *teletypewriter* (AE): Fernschreiber.
14 **ain't** (dial.): *isn't*.
16 **phony:** Schwindler(in).
20 **crap** (vulg.): Scheiße.

Benny had it on his mind to marry her, she don't go for it, Benny spent maybe thousands sending her to head-shrinkers. Even the famous one, the one can only speak German, boy, did he throw in the towel. You can't talk
5 her out of these" – he made a fist, as though to crush an intangible – "ideas. Try it sometime. Get her to tell you some of the stuff she believes. Mind you," he said, "I like the kid. Everybody does, but there's lots that don't. I do. I sincerely like the kid. I'm sensitive, that's why. You've
10 got to be sensitive to appreciate her: a streak of the poet. But I'll tell you the truth. You can beat your brains out for her, and she'll hand you horseshit on a platter. To give an example – who is she like you see her today? She's strictly a girl you'll read where she ends up at the bottom
15 of a bottle of Seconals. I've seen it happen more times than you've got toes: and those kids, they weren't even nuts. She's nuts."

"But young. And with a great deal of youth ahead of her."

20 "If you mean future, you're wrong again. Now a couple of years back, out on the Coast, there was a time it could've been different. She had something working for her, she had them interested, she could've really rolled.

---

1 **to go for s.th.** (fig.): auf etwas aus sein.
4 **to throw in the towel** (fig.): das Handtuch werfen.
6 **intangible:** nicht greifbar.
9 **sensitive:** feinfühlig.
10 **streak:** (fig.) Spur, Anflug.
11 **to beat one's brain out:** sich den Kopf zerbrechen.
12 **to hand s.o. horseshit on a platter** (slang): jdm. Räuberscheiße auf-tischen.
15 **Seconal:** Handelsname eines Psychopharmakons wie etwa Valium.
17 **to be nuts** (infml.): bekloppt sein.
21 **the Coast:** Gemeint ist die Westküste der USA.
23 **to roll:** (fig.) vorwärtskommen (AE).

But when you walk out on a thing like that, you don't
walk back. Ask Luise Rainer. And Rainer was a star.
Sure, Holly was no star; she never got out of the still
department. But that was before *The Story of Dr. Was-*
5 *sell.* Then she could've really rolled. I know, see, cause
I'm the guy was giving her the push." He pointed his cigar
at himself. "O. J. Berman."
He expected recognition, and I didn't mind obliging him,
it was all right by me, except I'd never heard of O. J.
10 Berman. It developed that he was a Hollywood actor's
agent.
"I'm the first one saw her. Out at Santa Anita[26]. She's
hanging around the track every day. I'm interested: pro-
fessionally. I find out she's some jock's regular, she's
15 living with the shrimp. I get the jock told Drop It if he
don't want conversation with the vice boys: see, the kid's
fifteen. But stylish: she's okay, she comes across. Even
when she's wearing glasses *this* thick; even when she
opens her mouth and you don't know if she's a hillbilly or
20 an Okie or what. I still don't. My guess, nobody'll ever

---

1 **to walk out on s.th.:** etwas im Stich lassen.
3f. **still department:** Abteilung für stumme (Film-)Rollen.
8 **to oblige s.o.:** jdm. einen Gefallen tun.
13 **to hang around:** herumhängen, -lungern.
  track: Rennbahn.
14 **jock:** Kurzform von *jockey*.
  regular: hier: feste Freundin.
15 **shrimp:** Kerlchen, Steppke.
16 **vice boys:** Knaben von der Sitte, Sittenpolizei.
17 **stylish:** elegant, im großen Stil.
  to come across (fig.): ,ankommen', wirken.
19 **hillbillie:** Hinterwäldler(in), Landpomeranze.
20 **Okie** (slang, pej.): Wanderarbeiter aus Oklahoma, Tagelöhner vom
  Dienst.

38

know where she came from. She's such a goddamn liar,
maybe she don't know herself any more. But it took us a
year to smooth out that accent. How we did it finally, we
gave her French lessons: after she could imitate French,
5 it wasn't so long she could imitate English. We modeled
her along the Margaret Sullavan[27] type, but she could
pitch some curves of her own, people were interested,
big ones, and to top it all, Benny Polan, a respected guy,
Benny wants to marry her. An agent could ask for more?
10 Then wham! *The Story of Dr. Wassell.* You see that picture? Cecil B. DeMille. Gary Cooper.[28] Jesus. I kill
myself, it's all set: they're going to test her for the part of
Dr. Wassell's nurse. One of his nurses, anyway. Then
wham! The phone rings." He picked a telephone out of
15 the air and held it to his ear. "She says, this is Holly, I say
honey, you sound far away, she says I'm in New York, I
say what the hell are you doing in New York when it's
Sunday and you got the test tomorrow? She says I'm in
New York cause I've never been to New York. I say get
20 your ass on a plane and get back here, she says I don't
want it. I say what's your angle, doll? She says you got to
want it to be good and I don't want it, I say well, what the
hell do you want, and she says when I find out you'll be
the first to know. See what I mean: horseshit on a
25 platter."
The red cat jumped off its crate and rubbed against his
leg. He lifted the cat on the toe of his shoe and gave him a

---

3 **to smooth out:** glätten; (fig.) ausbügeln.
7 **to pitch some curves of one's own:** wörtl.: sich Bogenwürfe werfen
  (Baseball); hier (fig.): etwa: sich eine günstige Position ausbauen.
10 **wham:** rums!, wumm!
20 **ass** (AE, vulg.): Arsch.
21 **angle:** hier: Meinung, Perspektive.

toss, which was hateful of him except he seemed not aware of the cat but merely his own irritableness.

"*This* is what she wants?" he said, flinging out his arms.

5 "A lot of characters they aren't expected? Living off tips. Running around with bums. So maybe she could marry Rusty Trawler? You should pin a medal on her for that?"

He waited, glaring.

"Sorry, I don't know him."

10 "You don't know Rusty Trawler, you can't know much about the kid. Bad deal," he said, his tongue clucking in his huge head. "I was hoping you maybe had influence. Could level with the kid before it's too late."

"But according to you, it already is."

15 He blew a smoke ring, let it fade before he smiled; the smile altered his face, made something gentle happen. "I could get it rolling again. Like I told you," he said, and now it sounded true, "I sincerely like the kid."

"What scandals are you spreading, O. J.?" Holly

20 splashed into the room, a towel more or less wrapped round her and her wet feet dripping footmarks on the floor.

"Just the usual. That you're nuts."

"Fred knows that already."

25 "But you don't."

---

2 **irritableness:** Gereiztheit.
4 **to live off s.th.:** von etwas leben.
5 **bum** (infml.): Penner, Gammler.
6 **to pin a medal on s.o.:** jdm. einen Orden anstecken.
8 **to glare:** starren.
11 **to cluck:** schnalzen.
13 **to level with s.o.:** mit jdm. ehrlich sein.
20 **to splash:** spritzen, flitzen.
21 **to drip:** tropfen lassen.

"Light me a cigarette, darling," she said, snatching off
a bathing cap and shaking her hair. "I don't mean you,
O. J. You're such a slob. You always nigger-lip."
She scooped up the cat and swung him onto her shoulder.
5 He perched there with the balance of a bird, his paws
tangled in her hair as if it were knitting yarn; and yet,
despite these amiable antics, it was a grim cat with a
pirate's cutthroat face; one eye was gluey-blind, the
other sparkled with dark deeds.
10 "O. J. is a slob," she told me, taking the cigarette I'd
lighted. "But he does know a terrific lot of phone num-
bers. What's David O. Selznick's[29] number, O. J.?"
"Lay off."
"It's not a joke, darling. I want you to call him up and tell
15 him what a genius Fred is. He's written barrels of the
most marvelous stories. Well, don't blush, Fred: you
didn't say you were a genius, I did. Come on, O. J. What
are you going to do to make Fred rich?"
"Suppose you let me settle that with Fred."
20 "Remember," she said, leaving us, "I'm his agent. Another thing: if I holler, come zipper me up. And if anybody knocks, let them in."

---

3 **slob** (slang): Dreckschwein, Schlampe.
   to nigger-lip: etwa: mit den (dicken) Lippen naß machen.
5 **to perch:** hocken, sitzen.
6 **yarn:** Garn.
7 **amiable:** liebenswert.
   antics: Possen, Eskapaden.
8 **cutthroat:** mörderisch, unbarmherzig.
   gluey-blind: klebrig-trüb.
13 **to lay off:** aufhören.
19 **to settle s.th. with s.o.:** etwas mit jdm. abmachen.
21 **to holler:** brüllen.
   to zipper s.o. up: jdm. den Reißverschluß hochziehen.

A multitude did. Within the next quarter-hour a stag party had taken over the apartment, several of them in uniform. I counted two Naval officers and an Air Force colonel; but they were outnumbered by graying arrivals
5 beyond draft status. Except for a lack of youth, the guests had no common theme, they seemed strangers among strangers; indeed, each face, on entering, had struggled to conceal dismay at seeing others there. It was as if the hostess had distributed her invitations while zig-zagging
10 through various bars; which was probably the case. After the initial frowns, however, they mixed without grumbling, especially O. J. Berman, who avidly exploited the new company to avoid discussing my Hollywood future. I was left abandoned by the bookshelves; of the books
15 there, more than half were about horses, the rest baseball. Pretending an interest in *Horseflesh and How to Tell It* gave me sufficiently private opportunity for sizing Holly's friends.
Presently one of these became prominent. He was a mid-
20 dle-aged child that had never shed its baby fat, though

---

1 **multitude:** Menge.
1f. **stag party:** Männerparty.
4 **colonel:** Oberst.
   to be outnumbered: in der Minderzahl sein.
   arrival: Ankömmling.
5 **draft status:** etwa: Einberufungsalter (*draft*: Einberufung [AE]).
8 **dismay:** Bestürzung.
9 **hostess:** Gastgeberin.
   to zig-zag: hier: herumziehen, (von einem Ort zum anderen) ziehen.
11 **initial:** anfänglich.
11f. **to grumble:** murren.
12 **avidly** (adv.): eifrig, mit Eifer.
   to exploit: ausnutzen.
18 **to size:** einordnen, einschätzen.

some gifted tailor had almost succeeded in camouflaging
his plump and spankable bottom. There wasn't a suspicion of bone in his body; his face, a zero filled in with
pretty miniature features, had an unused, a virginal qual-
5 ity: it was as if he'd been born, then expanded his skin
remaining unlined as a blown-up balloon, and his mouth,
though ready for squalls and tantrums, a spoiled sweet
puckering. But it was not appearance that singled him
out; preserved infants aren't all that rare. It was, rather,
10 his conduct; for he was behaving as though the party
were his: like an energetic octopus, he was shaking martinis, making introductions, manipulating the phonograph. In fairness, most of his activities were dictated by
the hostess herself: *Rusty, would you mind; Rusty, would*
15 *you please.* If he was in love with her, then clearly he had
his jealousy in check. A jealous man might have lost
control, watching her as she skimmed around the room,

1 **gifted:** begabt.
  to camouflage: tarnen.
2 **spankable** (infml.): versohlbar.
3 **zero:** Null.
4 **virginal:** jungfräulich.
6 **unlined:** 1. faltenlos; 2. ohne markante Züge.
7 **squall:** Sturm, Schrei.
  tantrum: Wutanfall, Koller.
8f. **to single s.o. out:** jdn. aussondern.
9 **preserved:** konserviert.
  infant: Kleinkind.
11 **energetic:** energiegeladen.
  octopus: Tintenfisch.
12 **to manipulate s.th.:** hier: etwas bedienen, an etwas herumhantieren.
12f. **phonograph** (AE, arch.): Plattenspieler.
16 **jealousy:** Eifersucht.
  in check: unter Kontrolle.
17 **to skim:** gleiten.

carrying her cat in one hand but leaving the other free to straighten a tie or remove lapel lint; the Air Force colonel wore a medal that came in for quite a polish.

The man's name was Rutherfurd ("Rusty") Trawler. In 1908 he'd lost both his parents, his father the victim of an anarchist and his mother of shock, which double misfortune had made Rusty an orphan, a millionaire, and a celebrity, all at the age of five. He'd been a stand-by of the Sunday supplements ever since, a consequence that had gathered hurricane momentum when, still a schoolboy, he had caused his godfather-custodian to be arrested on charges of sodomy. After that, marriage and divorce sustained his place in the tabloid-sun. His first wife had taken herself, and her alimony, to a rival of Father Divine's. The second wife seems unaccounted for, but the third had sued him in New York State with a full satchel of the kind of testimony that entails. He him-

---

2 **lint:** Fluse(n) (AE).
7 **orphan:** Waise.
8 **celebrity:** Berühmtheit, berühmte Person.
   to be a stand-by: (immer) bereit stehen.
9 **supplement:** Beilage (zu einer Zeitung).
10 **to gather momentum:** in Fahrt kommen.
11 **godfather-custodian:** Pate und Vormund.
12 **charge:** Anklage.
   sodomy: Sodomie (Geschlechtsverkehr mit Tieren).
13 **divorce:** (Ehe-)Scheidung.
   to sustain: aufrechterhalten.
14 **alimony:** Unterhaltszahlung.
15 **Father Divine:** Himmlischer Vater.
15f. **unaccounted for:** vermißt.
16 **to sue s.o.:** jdn. verklagen.
17 **satchel:** Ranzen.
   testimony: Beweis, Aussage.
   to entail: zur Folge haben.

44

self divorced the last Mrs. Trawler, his principal complaint stating that she'd started a mutiny aboard his yacht, said mutiny resulting in his being deposited on the Dry Tortugas. Though he'd been a bachelor since, apparently before the war he'd proposed to Unity Mitford, at least he was supposed to have sent her a cable offering to marry her if Hitler didn't.[30] This was said to be the reason Winchell always referred to him as a Nazi; that, and the fact that he attended rallies in Yorkville[31].

I was not told these things. I read them in *The Baseball Guide*, another selection off Holly's shelf which she seemed to use for a scrapbook. Tucked between the pages were Sunday features, together with scissored snippings from gossip columns. *Rusty Trawler and Holly Golightly two-on-the-aisle at "One Touch of Venus" preem*. Holly came up from behind, and caught me read-

---

1 **to divorce s.o.:** sich von jdm. scheiden.
2 **mutiny:** Meuterei.
   aboard: an Bord.
3 **said:** besagte(r).
   to deposit: hier: aussetzen.
4 **Dry Tortugas:** Gruppe von acht zu Florida gehörigen, wasserlosen Koralleninseln am Eingang des Golfs von Mexiko.
5 **to propose to s.o.:** jdm. einen Heiratsantrag machen.
9 **rally:** Massenversammlung.
11 **selection:** Auswahl.
12 **scrapbook:** Sammelalbum.
   tucked: hineingesteckt.
13 **feature:** Feature, (aktueller) Bericht.
   to scissor: herausschneiden.
14 **snipping:** (Zeitungs-)Ausschnitt.
   gossip column: Klatschkolumne.
15 **two-on-the-aisle:** von *to roll in the aisles:* etwa: sich vor Lachen kugeln (*aisle:* Gang [in einem Theater o. ä.]).
16 **preem** (slang): Premiere.

ing: *Miss Holiday Golightly, of the Boston Golightlys, making every day a holiday for the 24-karat Rusty Trawler.*

"Admiring my publicity, or are you just a baseball fan?" she said, adjusting her dark glasses as she glanced over my shoulder.

I said, "What was this week's weather report?"

She winked at me, but it was humorless: a wink of warning, "I'm all for horses, but I loathe baseball," she said, and the sub-message in her voice was saying she wished me to forget she'd ever mentioned Sally Tomato. "I hate the sound of it on a radio, but I have to listen, it's part of my research. There're so few things men can talk about. If a man doesn't like baseball, then he must like horses, and if he doesn't like either of them, well, I'm in trouble anyway: he don't like girls. And how are you making out with O. J.?"

"We've separated by mutual agreement."

"He's an opportunity, believe me."

"I do believe you. But what have I to offer that would strike him as an opportunity?"

She persisted. "Go over there and make him think he isn't funny-looking. He really can help you, Fred."

"I understand you weren't too appreciative." She

---

1 **Boston Golightlys:** vermutl. Name einer Baseballmannschaft.
2 **24-karat:** vierundzwanzigkarätig, hochkarätig.
5 **to adjust:** richten, zurechtrücken.
8 **to wink at s.o.:** jdm. zuzwinkern.
10 **sub-message:** Botschaft zwischen den Zeilen.
13 **research:** Forschung.
16f. **to make out with s.o.:** mit jdm. zurechtkommen.
18 **mutual agreement:** gegenseitiges Einvernehmen.
24 **to be appreciative:** dankbar sein, (etwas) zu schätzen wissen.

seemed puzzled until I said: *"The Story of Doctor Wassell."*

"He's still harping?" she said, and cast across the room an affectionate look at Berman. "But he's got a point, I *should* feel guilty. Not because they would have given me the part or because I would have been good: they wouldn't and I wouldn't. If I do feel guilty, I guess it's because I let him go on dreaming when I wasn't dreaming a bit. I was just vamping for time to make a few self-improvements: I knew damn well I'd never be a movie star. It's too hard; and if you're intelligent, it's too embarrassing. My complexes aren't inferior enough: being a movie star and having a big fat ego are supposed to go hand-in-hand; actually, it's essential not to have any ego at all. I don't mean I'd mind being rich and famous. That's very much on my schedule, and someday I'll try to get around to it; but if it happens, I'd like to have my ego tagging along. I want to still be me when I wake up one fine morning and have breakfast at Tiffany's. You need a glass," she said, noticing my empty hands. "Rusty! Will you bring my friend a drink?"

She was still hugging the cat. "Poor slob," she said, tickling his head, "poor slob without a name. It's a little inconvenient, his not having a name. But I haven't any right to give him one: he'll have to wait until he *belongs* to

---

3 **to harp** (*on s.th.*): auf etwas herumreiten.
9 **to vamp for time:** auf Zeit spielen, improvisieren, um Zeit zu gewinnen.
13 **ego:** Ego, Selbstbewußtsein.
16 **schedule:** (fig.) Fahrplan.
18 **to tag along:** mitzockeln.
24 **inconvenient:** ungelegen, unbequem.

somebody. We just sort of took up by the river one day, we don't belong to each other: he's an independent, and so am I. I don't want to own anything until I know I've found the place where me and things belong together. I'm not quite sure where that is just yet. But I know what it's like." She smiled, and let the cat drop to the floor. "It's like Tiffany's," she said. "Not that I give a hoot about jewelry. Diamonds, yes. But it's tacky to wear diamonds before you're forty; and even that's risky. They only look right on the really old girls. Maria Ouspenskaya.[32] Wrinkles and bones, white hair and diamonds: I can't wait. But that's not why I'm mad about Tiffany's. Listen. You know those days when you've got the mean reds?"

"Same as the blues?"

"No," she said slowly. "No, the blues are because you're getting fat or maybe it's been raining too long. You're sad, that's all. But the mean reds are horrible. You're afraid and you sweat like hell, but you don't know what you're afraid of. Except something bad is going to happen, only you don't know what it is. You've had that feeling?"

"Quite often. Some people call it *angst*."

"All right. *Angst*. But what do you do about it?"

"Well, a drink helps."

---

1 **to take up with s.o.** (infml.): sich mit jdm. anfreunden.
7f. **to give a hoot about s.th.:** sich nicht die Bohne für etwas interessieren.
8 **jewelry:** Juwelen, Schmuck.
  tacky (AE, infml.): ordinär, vulgär.
11 **wrinkle:** Falte.
14 **the mean reds:** wörtl.: die miesen Roten; hier: Weltangst, Existenzangst (*mean:* mies, schäbig, gemein).
15 **blues** (pl.): depressive Stimmung, Moralischer.

"I've tried that. I've tried aspirin, too. Rusty thinks I should smoke marijuana, and I did for a while, but it only makes me giggle. What I've found does the most good is just to get into a taxi and go to Tiffany's. It calms me
5 down right away, the quietness and the proud look of it; nothing very bad could happen to you there, not with those kind men in their nice suits, and that lovely smell of silver and alligator wallets. If I could find a real-life place that made me feel like Tiffany's, then I'd buy some furni-
10 ture and give the cat a name. I've thought maybe after the war, Fred and I –" She pushed up her dark glasses, and her eyes, the differing colors of them, the grays and wisps of blue and green, had taken on a far-seeing sharpness. "I went to Mexico once. It's wonderful country for
15 raising horses. I saw one place near the sea. Fred's good with horses."

Rusty Trawler came carrying a martini: he handed it over without looking at me. "I'm hungry," he announced, and his voice, retarded as the rest of him, produced an
20 unnerving brat-whine that seemed to blame Holly. "It's seven-thirty, and I'm hungry. You know what the doctor said."

"Yes, Rusty. I know what the doctor said."

"Well, then break it up. Let's go."

25 "I want you to behave, Rusty." She spoke softly, but

---

2 **marijuana:** Marihuana (Rauschgift).
3 **to giggle:** kichern.
8 **alligator wallet:** Kroko-Brieftasche.
13 **wisp:** hier: Äderchen.
19 **retarded:** (fig.) zurückgeblieben.
20 **unnerving:** nervtötend, enervierend.
  brat-whine: Görengequengel (*brat:* Göre).
24 **to break s.th. up:** etwas abbrechen.

there was a governess threat of punishment in her tone
that caused an odd flush of pleasure, of gratitude, to pink
his face.

"You don't love me," he complained, as though they
5 were alone.

"Nobody loves naughtiness."

Obviously she'd said what he wanted to hear; it appeared
to both excite and relax him. Still he continued, as
though it were a ritual: "Do you love me?"

10 She patted him. "Tend to your chores, Rusty. And when
I'm ready, we'll go eat wherever you want."

"Chinatown[33]?"

"But that doesn't mean sweet and sour spareribs. You
know what the doctor said."

15 As he returned to his duties with a satisfied waddle, I
couldn't resist reminding her that she hadn't answered
his question. "*Do* you love him?"

"I told you: you can make yourself love anybody.
Besides, he had a stinking childhood."

20 "If it was so stinking, why does he cling to it?"

"Use your head. Can't you see it's just that Rusty feels
safer in diapers than he would in a skirt? Which is really
the choice, only he's awfully touchy about it. He tried to

---

1 **governess:** gouvernantenähnlich.
2 **flush:** Schwall.
  gratitude: Dankbarkeit.
  to pink: rosa färben.
6 **naughtiness:** Ungezogenheit.
10 **to tend to chores:** Arbeiten erledigen.
13 **spareribs** (pl.): Rippchen.
15 **waddle:** Watscheln.
22 **diaper:** Windel (AE).
23 **touchy:** leicht reizbar.

stab me with a butter knife because I told him to grow up
and face the issue, settle down and play house with a nice
fatherly truck driver. Meantime, I've got him on my
hands; which is okay, he's harmless, he thinks girls are
5 dolls literally."

"Thank God."

"Well, if it were true of most men, I'd hardly be thanking
God."

"I meant thank God you're not going to marry Mr.
10 Trawler."

She lifted an eyebrow. "By the way, I'm not pretending I
don't know he's rich. Even land in Mexico costs something. Now," she said, motioning me forward, "let's get
hold of O. J."

15 I held back while my mind worked to win a postponement. Then I remembered: "Why *Traveling?*"

"On my card?" she said, disconcerted. "You think it's
funny?"

"Not funny. Just provocative."

20 She shrugged. "After all, how do I know where I'll be
living tomorrow? So I told them to put *Traveling.* Anyway, it was a waste of money, ordering those cards.
Except I felt I owed it to them to buy some little *some-*
thing. They're from Tiffany's." She reached for my mar-
25 tini, I hadn't touched it; she drained it in two swallows,

---

  1 **to stab:** erstechen.
  2 **to face the issue:** der Sache ins Gesicht sehen.
    to play house: (eine Wohnung wie eine) Puppenstube einrichten.
  3 **truck driver:** Lastwagenfahrer.
  3f. **to get s.o. on one's hands:** jdn. ‚am Hals haben'.
  5 **literally** (adv.): buchstäblich, wörtlich.
 15f. **postponement:** Aufschub.
 19 **provocative:** provokativ, provozierend.
 25 **to drain:** leeren.

and took my hand. "Quit stalling. You're going to make friends with O. J."

An occurrence at the door intervened. It was a young woman, and she entered like a wind-rush, a squall of scarves and jangling gold. "H-H-Holly," she said, wagging a finger as she advanced, "you miserable h-h-hoarder. Hogging all these simply r-r-riveting m-m-men!"

She was well over six feet, taller than most men there. They straightened their spines, sucked in their stomachs; there was a general contest to match her swaying height.

Holly said, "What are you doing here?" and her lips were taut as drawn string.

"Why, n-n-nothing, sugar. I've been upstairs working with Yunioshi. Christmas stuff for the *Ba-ba-zaar*[34]. But you sound vexed, sugar?" She scattered a roundabout smile. "You b-b-boys not vexed at me for butting in on your p-p-party?"

---

1 **to stall** (AE, slang): Hinhaltetaktik anwenden, sich stur stellen.
3 **occurrence:** Vorfall.
   to intervene: dazwischenkommen.
4 **wind-rush:** Windzug.
5 **jangling:** klimpernd.
5 f. **to wag s.th.:** mit etwas wackeln.
6 f. **hoarder:** jd., der etwas hortet, Hamsterer.
7 **to hog** (infml.): in Beschlag nehmen.
   riveting: hinreißend.
9 **spine:** Rückgrat.
   to suck in: (Luft) einziehen.
10 **contest:** Wettkampf.
   to match s.th.: es mit etwas aufnehmen.
13 **taut:** gespannt, straff.
16 **vexed:** verärgert.
   roundabout: im Kreis herum, kreisförmig.
17 **to butt in on s.th.** (infml.): in etwas hineinplatzen.

Rusty Trawler tittered. He squeezed her arm, as though to admire her muscle, and asked her if she could use a drink.

"I surely could," she said. "Make mine bourbon."

5 Holly told her, "There *isn't* any." Whereupon the Air Force colonel suggested he run out for a bottle.

"Oh, I declare, don't let's have a f-f-fuss. I'm happy with ammonia. Holly, honey," she said, slightly shoving her, "don't you bother about me. I can introduce myself."

10 She stooped toward O. J. Berman, who, like many short men in the presence of tall women, had an aspiring mist in his eye. "I'm Mag W-w-wildwood, from Wild-w-w-wood, Arkansas. That's hill country."

It seemed a dance, Berman performing some fancy foot-
15 work to prevent his rivals cutting in. He lost her to a quadrille of partners who gobbled up her stammered jokes like popcorn tossed to pigeons. It was a comprehensible success. She was a triumph over ugliness, so often more beguiling than real beauty, if only because it
20 contains paradox. In this case, as opposed to the scrupu-

---

1 **to titter:** kichern.
to squeeze: drücken.
7 **to declare:** hier: beteuern.
8 **ammonia:** eigtl.: Ammoniak; gemeint ist hier Sodawasser, zu dessen Herstellung Ammoniak als Hilfsstoff benötigt wird.
to shove: schieben, schubsen.
11 **aspiring:** hochstrebend.
14 f. **fancy footwork:** kunstvolle Beinarbeit.
15 **to cut in:** sich einschalten.
16 **quadrille:** Quadrille (Vierpaartanz im ¾- oder ⁶⁄₈-Takt).
to gobble up: (fig.) verschlingen.
to stammer: stottern.
17 f. **comprehensible:** verständlich.
19 **to beguile:** betören.
20 f. **scrupulous:** gewissenhaft.

lous method of plain good taste and scientific grooming, the trick had been worked by exaggerating defects; she'd made them ornamental by admitting them boldly. Heels that emphasized her height, so steep her ankles trembled; a flat tight bodice that indicated she could go to a beach in bathing trunks; hair that was pulled straight back, accentuating the spareness, the starvation of her fashion-model face. Even the stutter, certainly genuine but still a bit laid on, had been turned to advantage. It was the master stroke, that stutter; for it contrived to make her banalities sound somehow original, and secondly, despite her tallness, her assurance, it served to inspire in male listeners a protective feeling. To illustrate: Berman had to be pounded on the back because she said, "Who can tell me w-w-where is the j-j-john?"; then, completing the cycle, he offered an arm to guide her himself.

1 **grooming:** gepflegtes Äußeres.
2 **to exaggerate:** übertreiben.
4 **to emphasize:** betonen, unterstreichen.
  ankle: Knöchel.
5 **bodice:** Oberteil (eines Kleides).
6 **bathing trunks** (pl.): Badehose.
7 **to accentuate:** akzentuieren, betonen.
  spareness: Magerkeit.
  starvation: Ausgehungertheit.
8 **fashion-model:** Mannequin, Fotomodell.
9 **to lay on:** (Farbe) auftragen.
  to turn to advantage: zum Vorteil wenden.
10 **master stroke:** Geniestreich.
  to contrive: fertigbringen, schaffen.
12 **assurance:** Selbstvertrauen.
13 **protective:** beschützend.
14 **to pound:** (kräftig) schlagen.
16 **cycle:** hier: Routine.

"That," said Holly, "won't be necessary. She's been here before. She knows where it is." She was emptying ashtrays, and after Mag Wildwood had left the room, she emptied another, then said, sighed rather: "It's really
5 very sad." She paused long enough to calculate the number of inquiring expressions; it was sufficient. "And so mysterious. You'd think it would show more. But heaven knows, she *looks* healthy. So, well, *clean*. That's the extraordinary part. Wouldn't you," she asked with
10 concern, but of no one in particular, "wouldn't you say she *looked* clean?"
Someone coughed, several swallowed. A Naval officer, who had been holding Mag Wildwood's drink, put it down.
15 "But then," said Holly, "I hear so many of these Southern girls have the same trouble." She shuddered delicately, and went to the kitchen for more ice.
Mag Wildwood couldn't understand it, the abrupt absence of warmth on her return; the conversations she
20 began behaved like green logs, they fumed but would not fire. More unforgivably, people were leaving without taking her telephone number. The Air Force colonel decamped while her back was turned, and this was the straw too much: he'd asked her to dinner. Suddenly she
25 was blind. And since gin to artifice bears the same rela-

16 **to shudder:** zittern, erschaudern.
20 **green log:** grünes (daher schwer brennbares) Holz.
   to fume: rauchen, qualmen.
21 **unforgivably** (adv.): unverzeihlich.
23 **to decamp** (infml.): sich aus dem Staub machen, seine Zelte abbrechen.
23 f. **to be the straw too much** (fig.): das Faß zum Überlaufen bringen.
25 **artifice:** List.

tion as tears to mascara, her attractions at once dissembled. She took it out on everyone. She called her hostess a Hollywood degenerate. She invited a man in his fifties to fight. She told Berman, Hitler was right. She exhila-
5 rated Rusty Trawler by stiff-arming him into a corner. "You know what's going to happen to you?" she said, with no hint of a stutter. "I'm going to march you over to the zoo and feed you to the yak." He looked altogether willing, but she disappointed him by sliding to the floor,
10 where she sat humming.

"You're a bore. Get up from there," Holly said, stretching on a pair of gloves. The remnants of the party were waiting at the door, and when the bore didn't budge Holly cast me an apologetic glance. "Be an angel, would
15 you, Fred? Put her in a taxi. She lives at the Winslow[35]."

"Don't. Live Barbizon[36]. Regent 4-5700. Ask for Mag Wildwood."

"You *are* an angel, Fred."
20 They were gone. The prospect of steering an Amazon

---

1 **mascara:** Maskara, Wimperntusche.
1 f. **to dissemble:** hier: sich ins Gegenteil verkehren.
2 **to take it out on s.o.:** sich an jdm. abreagieren.
3 **degenerate:** degenerierter Mensch, Entartete(r).
4 f. **to exhilarate:** freudig erregen.
5 **to stiff-arm:** mit steifen Armen schieben.
8 **yak:** Jak, tibetanisches Rind.
10 **to hum:** summen.
11 **bore:** Langweiler.
11 f. **to stretch on:** anziehen, überstreifen.
12 **remnants:** Überreste.
13 **to budge:** sich rühren.
14 **apologetic:** entschuldigend.
20 **Amazon:** Amazone (in der griechischen Mythologie Angehörige eines weiblichen Kriegervolks).

into a taxi obliterated whatever resentment I felt. But she solved the problem herself. Rising on her own steam, she stared down at me with a lurching loftiness. She said, "Let's go Stork[37]. Catch lucky balloon," and fell full-
5 length like an axed oak. My first thought was to run for a doctor. But examination proved her pulse fine and her breathing regular. She was simply asleep. After finding a pillow for her head, I left her to enjoy it.

*

The following afternoon I collided with Holly on the
10 stairs. *"You"*, she said, hurrying past with a package from the druggist. "There she is, on the verge of pneumonia. A hang-over out to here. And the mean reds on top of it." I gathered from this that Mag Wildwood was still in the apartment, but she gave me no chance to
15 explore her surprising sympathy. Over the weekend, mystery deepened. First, there was the Latin who came to my door: mistakenly, for he was inquiring after Miss Wildwood. It took a while to correct his error, our accents seemed mutually incoherent, but by the time we

---

1 **to obliterate:** auslöschen.
2 **on one's own steam:** mit eigener Hilfe.
3 **lurching:** schlingernd.
  loftiness: Hochmut.
4 **lucky balloon:** etwa: Glücksballon (für eine Reise ins Glück).
5 **axed:** (mit der Axt) gefällt.
9 **to collide:** zusammenstoßen.
11 **druggist:** Apotheker (AE).
  verge: Rand.
11 f. **pneumonia:** Lungenentzündung.
12 **hang-over:** Kater (Folge übermäßigen Alkoholgenusses).
16 **Latin:** hier: Lateinamerikaner.
19 **incoherent:** schwer verständlich.

had I was charmed. He'd been put together with care, his brown head and bullfighter's figure had an exactness, a perfection, like an apple, an orange, something nature has made just right. Added to this, as decoration, were
5 an English suit and a brisk cologne and, what is still more unlatin, a bashful manner. The second event of the day involved him again. It was toward evening, and I saw him on my way out to dinner. He was arriving in a taxi; the driver helped him totter into the house with a load of
10 suitcases. That gave me something to chew on: by Sunday my jaws were quite tired.
Then the picture became both darker and clearer.
Sunday was an Indian summer day, the sun was strong, my window was open, and I heard voices on the fire
15 escape. Holly and Mag were sprawled there on a blanket, the cat between them. Their hair, newly washed, hung lankly. They were busy, Holly varnishing her toenails, Mag knitting on a sweater. Mag was speaking.
"If you ask me, I think you're l-l-lucky. At least there's
20 one thing you can say for Rusty. He's an American."
"Bully for him."
"*Sugar*. There's a war on."

2 **bullfighter:** Stierkämpfer.
5 **brisk:** frisch.
6 **bashful:** verschämt, schüchtern.
7 **to involve s.o.:** jdn. (in etwas) verwickeln.
9 **to totter:** schwanken, taumeln.
13 **Indian summer:** Altweibersommer (schönste und trockenste Jahreszeit in New York).
15 **to sprawl:** ausgestreckt liegen, sich rekeln.
17 **lankly** (adv.): strähnig.
   to varnish: lackieren.
18 **sweater:** Pullover.
21 **bully for him** (infml.): etwa: bravo!, gut gemacht!

"And when it's over, you've seen the last of me, boy."

"I don't feel that way. I'm p-p-proud of my country. The men in my family were great soldiers. There's a statue of Papadaddy Wildwood smack in the center of Wildwood."

"Fred's a soldier," said Holly. "But I doubt if he'll ever be a statue. Could be. They say the more stupid you are the braver. He's pretty stupid."

"Fred's that boy upstairs? I didn't realize he was a soldier. But he *does* look stupid."

"Yearning. Not stupid. He wants awfully to be on the inside staring out: anybody with their nose pressed against a glass is liable to look stupid. Anyhow, he's a different Fred. Fred's my brother."

"You call your own f-f-flesh and b-b-blood stupid?"

"If he is he is."

"Well, it's poor taste to say so. A boy that's fighting for you and me and all of us."

"What is this: a bond rally?"

"I just want you to know where I stand. I appreciate a joke, but underneath I'm a s-s-serious person. Proud to be an American. That's why I'm sorry about José." She put down her knitting needles. "You *do* think he's terribly good-looking, don't you?" Holly said Hmn, and swiped the cat's whiskers with her lacquer brush. "If only I could get used to the idea of m-m-marrying a Brazilian.

---

4 **smack** (adv.): direkt.
13 **to be liable to do s.th.:** leicht etwas tun.
19 **bond rally:** Massenversammlung zur Einwerbung von Zeichnern von Kriegsanleihen, sogenannten »Liberty Bonds«.
25 **to swipe:** schlagen.
   whiskers: Schnurrbart(haare).
   lacquer: Nagellack.

And *being* a B-b-brazilian myself. It's such a canyon to
cross. Six thousand miles, and not knowing the language –"
"Go to Berlitz."
5 "Why on earth would they be teaching P-p-portu-
guese?[38] It isn't as though anyone spoke it. No, my only
chance is to try and make José forget politics and become
an American. It's such a useless thing for a man to want
to be: the p-p-president of *Brazil*." She sighed and
10 picked up her knitting. "I must be madly in love. You saw
us together. Do you think I'm madly in love?"
"Well. Does he bite?"
Mag dropped a stitch. "Bite?"
"You. In bed."
15 "Why, no. *Should* he?" Then she added, censoriously:
"But he does laugh."
"Good. That's the right spirit. I like a man who sees the
humor; most of them, they're all pant and puff."
Mag withdrew her complaint; she accepted the comment
20 as flattery reflecting on herself. "Yes. I suppose."
"Okay. He doesn't bite. He laughs. What else?"
Mag counted up her dropped stitch and began again,
knit, purl, purl.
"I said –"
25 "I heard you. And it isn't that I don't want to tell you. But

---

1 f. **a canyon to cross** (fig.): ein Sprung ins Ungewisse.
  4 **Berlitz:** weltweites Fremdsprachenlehrinstitut.
 13 **to drop a stitch:** eine Masche (beim Stricken) fallen lassen.
 15 **censoriously** (adv.): strafend.
 18 **pant:** Keuchen; Herzklopfen.
    puff: Pusten; (slang) Feigling.
 20 **flattery:** Schmeichelei.
 23 **to purl:** links stricken.

it's so difficult to remember. I don't d-d-dwell on these things. The way you seem to. They go out of my head like a dream. I'm sure that's the n-n-normal attitude."

"It may be normal, darling; but I'd rather be natural."

Holly paused in the process of reddening the rest of the cat's whiskers. "Listen. If you can't remember, try leaving the lights on."

"Please understand me, Holly. I'm a very-very-very *conventional* person."

"Oh, balls. What's wrong with a decent look at a guy you like? Men are beautiful, a lot of them are, José is, and if you don't even want to *look* at him, well, I'd say he's getting a pretty cold plate of macaroni."

"L-l-lower your voice."

"You can't possibly be in love with him. Now. Does that answer your question?"

"No. Because I'm not a cold plate of m-m-macaroni. I'm a warm-hearted person. It's the basis of my character."

"Okay. You've got a warm heart. But if I were a man on my way to bed, I'd rather take along a hot-water bottle. It's more tangible."

"You won't hear any squawks out of José," she said complacently, her needles flashing in the sunlight. "What's more, I *am* in love with him. Do you realize I've knitted ten pairs of Argyles in less than three months? And this is the second sweater." She stretched the sweater and

---

1 **to dwell on s.th.:** bei etwas verweilen, viel über etwas nachdenken.
10 **balls** (pl., vulg.): Scheiße.
20 **hot-water bottle:** Wärmflasche.
21 **tangible:** greifbar.
22 **squawk** (infml.): Protest (wörtl.: Gackern).
22 f. **complacently** (adv.): selbstgefällig.
25 **Argyles:** Socken in rautenförmigem Schottenkaro.

tossed it aside. "What's the point, though? Sweaters in Brazil. I ought to be making s-s-sun helmets."

Holly lay back and yawned. "It must be winter some-time."

"It *rains*, that I know. Heat. Rain. J-j-jungles."

"Heat. Jungles. Actually, I'd like that."

"Better you than me."

"Yes," said Holly, with a sleepiness that was not sleepy. "Better me than you."

*

On Monday, when I went down for the morning mail, the card on Holly's box had been altered, a name added: Miss Golightly and Miss Wildwood were now traveling together. This might have held my interest longer except for a letter in my own mailbox. It was from a small university review to whom I'd sent a story. They liked it; and, though I must understand they could not afford to pay, they intended to publish. Publish: that meant *print*. Dizzy with excitement is no mere phrase. I had to tell someone: and, taking the stairs two at a time, I pounded on Holly's door.

I didn't trust my voice to tell the news; as soon as she came to the door, her eyes squinty with sleep, I thrust the letter at her. It seemed as though she'd had time to read sixty pages before she handed it back. "I wouldn't let them do it, not if they don't pay you," she said, yawning. Perhaps my face explained she'd misconstrued, that I'd

5 **jungle:** Dschungel.
15 **review:** (literatur-)wissenschaftliche Zeitschrift.
18 **dizzy:** schwindelig.
22 **squinty:** schielend, scheel.
22 f. **to thrust s.th. at s.o.:** jdm. etwas entgegenstrecken.
26 **to misconstrue:** mißverstehen, fehldeuten.

not wanted advice but congratulations: her mouth
shifted from a yawn into a smile. "Oh, I see. It's wonderful. Well, come in," she said. "We'll make a pot of coffee
and celebrate. No. I'll get dressed and take you to
5 lunch."
Her bedroom was consistent with her parlor: it perpetu-
ated the same camping-out atmosphere; crates and suitcases, everything packed and ready to go, like the belongings of a criminal who feels the law not far behind. In
10 the parlor there was no conventional furniture, but the
bedroom had the bed itself, a double one at that, and
quite flashy: blond wood, tufted satin.
She left the door of the bathroom open, and conversed
from there; between the flushing and the brushing, most
15 of what she said was unintelligible, but the gist of it was:
she *supposed* I knew Mag Wildwood had moved in, and
wasn't that *convenient?* because if you're going to *have* a
roommate, and she *isn't* a dyke, then the next best thing
is a *perfect* fool, which Mag *was*, because then you can
20 dump the lease on them *and* send them out for the
laundry.

---

6 **consistent:** passend.
  parlor (arch.): Salon, Wohnzimmer.
6f. **to perpetuate:** fortsetzen, aufrechterhalten (wörtl.: verewigen).
8f. **belongings** (pl.): Habe, Zubehör.
12 **flashy:** auffällig.
  blond: hier: hell.
  tufted: hier: mit Polsterknöpfen (festgemacht).
  satin: Satin (glänzendes Atlasgewebe).
13 **to converse:** sich unterhalten.
15 **unintelligible:** unverständlich.
  gist: (fig.) Kern, Wesentliches.
20 **to dump:** abladen.
  lease: Miete.

One could see that Holly had a laundry problem; the room was strewn, like a girls' gymnasium.

"– and you know, she's quite a successful model: isn't that *fan*tastic? But a good thing," she said, hobbling out of the bathroom as she adjusted a garter. "It ought to keep her out of my hair most of the day. And there shouldn't be too much trouble on the man front. She's engaged. Nice guy, too. Though there's a tiny difference in height: I'd say a foot, her favor. Where the hell –" She was on her knees poking under the bed. After she'd found what she was looking for, a pair of lizard shoes, she had to search for a blouse, a belt, and it was a subject to ponder, how, from such wreckage, she evolved the eventual effect: pampered, calmly immaculate, as though she'd been attended by Cleopatra's maids.[39] She said, "Listen," and cupped her hand under my chin, "I'm glad about the story. Really I am."

*

---

2 **strewn:** übersät.
   gymnasium: Turnhalle.
4 **to hobble:** humpeln.
5 **garter:** Strumpfband.
6 **to keep s.o. out of one's hair** (infml.): sich jdn. nicht auf den Wecker gehen lassen.
9 **her favor:** *in her favor:* zu ihren Gunsten.
11 **lizard:** Eidechse.
13 **to ponder:** nachdenken.
   wreckage: (fig.) Trümmer.
   to evolve: entfalten, entwickeln.
13 f. **eventual:** schließlich.
14 **pampered:** verwöhnt, verhätschelt.
   immaculate: makellos.
16 **to cup:** (gewölbt) halten.

That Monday in October, 1943. A beautiful day with the
buoyancy of a bird. To start, we had Manhattans at Joe
Bell's; and, when he heard of my good luck, champagne
cocktails on the house. Later, we wandered toward Fifth
Avenue,[40] where there was a parade. The flags in the
wind, the thump of military bands and military feet,
seemed to have nothing to do with war, but to be, rather,
a fanfare arranged in my personal honor.

We ate lunch at the cafeteria in the park. Afterwards,
avoiding the zoo (Holly said she couldn't bear to see
anything in a cage), we giggled, ran, sang along the paths
toward the old wooden boathouse, now gone. Leaves
floated on the lake; on the shore, a park-man was fanning
a bonfire of them, and the smoke, rising like Indian sig-
nals, was the only smudge on the quivering air. Aprils
have never meant much to me, autumns seem that season
of beginning, spring; which is how I felt sitting with Holly
on the railings of the boathouse porch. I thought of the
future, and spoke of the past. Because Holly wanted to
know about my childhood. She talked of her own, too;
but it was elusive, nameless, placeless, an impressionis-
tic[41] recital, though the impression received was contrary

2 **buoyancy:** Schwung, Leichtigkeit.
  Manhattan: Cocktail aus drei Vierteln Whisky, einem Viertel Wer-
  mut und einem Spritzer Magenbitter.
4 **on the house:** vom Wirt spendiert.
6 **thump:** Krachen, Dröhnen.
13 **to fan:** entfachen.
14 **bonfire:** Freudenfeuer.
15 **smudge:** (Schmutz-)Fleck.
  quivering: zitternd, flimmernd.
18 **porch:** Veranda (AE).
21 **elusive:** ausweichend.
22 **recital:** Vortrag.

to what one expected, for she gave an almost voluptuous
account of swimming and summer, Christmas trees,
pretty cousins, and parties: in short, happy in a way that
she was not, and never, certainly, the background of a
5 child who had run away.
Or, I asked, wasn't it true that she'd been out on her own
since she was fourteen? She rubbed her nose. "That's
true. The other isn't. But really, darling, you made such a
tragedy out of *your* childhood I didn't feel I should com-
10 pete."
She hopped off the railing. "Anyway, it reminds me: I
ought to send Fred some peanut butter." The rest of the
afternoon we were east and west worming out of reluctant grocers cans of peanut butter, a wartime scarcity;
15 dark came before we'd rounded up a half-dozen jars, the
last at a delicatessen on Third Avenue. It was near the
antique shop with the palace of a bird cage in its window,
so I took her there to see it, and she enjoyed the point, its
fantasy: "But still, it's a cage."
20 Passing a Woolworth's, she gripped my arm: "Let's steal
something," she said, pulling me into the store, where at
once there seemed a pressure of eyes, as though we were
already under suspicion. "Come on. Don't be chicken."
She scouted a counter piled with paper pumkins and Hal-

---

1 **voluptuous**: sinnlich.
13 **to worm s.th. out of s.o.**: jdm. etwas entlocken, jdm. etwas aus der
Nase ziehen.
13f. **reluctant**: widerwillig.
14 **scarcity**: Rarität, Seltenheit.
15 **to round up**: zusammentragen.
16 **delicatessen**: Delikatessengeschäft.
23 **chicken** (slang): feige.
24 **to scout**: auskundschaften.
pumpkin: Kürbis.

loween masks.[42] The saleslady was occupied with a group of nuns who were trying on masks. Holly picked up a mask and slipped it over her face; she chose another and put it on mine; then she took my hand and we walked
5 away. It was as simple as that. Outside, we ran a few blocks, I think to make it more dramatic; but also because, as I'd discovered, successful theft exhilarates. I wondered if she'd often stolen. "I used to," she said. "I mean I had to. If I wanted anything. But I still do it every
0 now and then, sort of to keep my hand in."
We wore the masks all the way home.

*

I have a memory of spending many hither and yonning days with Holly; and it's true, we did at odd moments see a great deal of each other; but on the whole, the memory
5 is false. Because toward the end of the month I found a job: what is there to add? The less the better, except to say it was necessary and lasted from nine to five. Which made our hours, Holly's and mine, extremely different.
0 Unless it was Thursday, her Sing Sing day, or unless she'd gone horseback riding in the park, as she did occasionally, Holly was hardly up when I came home. Sometimes, stopping there, I shared her wake-up coffee while she dressed for the evening. She was forever on her way
5 out, not always with Rusty Trawler, but usually, and usually, too, they were joined by Mag Wildwood and the

---

1 **saleslady:** Verkäuferin.
7 **theft:** Diebstahl.
10 **to keep one's hand in** (infml.): in Übung bleiben.
12 **hither and yonning:** da- und dorthin ziehend (abgeleitet aus dem Adverb *hither and yon[der]*).

handsome Brazilian, whose name was José Ybarra-
Jaegar: his mother was German. As a quartet, they
struck an unmusical note, primarily the fault of Ybarra-
Jaegar, who seemed as out of place in their company as a
5 violin in a jazz band. He was intelligent, he was present-
able, he appeared to have a serious link with his work,
which was obscurely governmental, vaguely important,
and took him to Washington several days a week. How,
then, could he survive night after night in La Rue, El
10 Morocco,[43] listening to the Wildwood ch-ch-chatter and
staring into Rusty's raw baby-buttocks face? Perhaps,
like most of us in a foreign country, he was incapable of
placing people, selecting a frame for their picture, as he
would at home; therefore all Americans had to be judged
15 in a pretty equal light, and on this basis his companions
appeared to be tolerable examples of local color and
national character. That would explain much; Holly's
determination explains the rest.
Late one afternoon, while waiting for a Fifth Avenue
20 bus, I noticed a taxi stop across the street to let out a girl
who ran up the steps of the Forty-second Street public
library. She was through the doors before I recognized
her, which was pardonable, for Holly and libraries were

---

3 **to strike an unmusical note:** nicht harmonieren, nicht zusammen-
passen.
   primarily (adv.): vorwiegend, hauptsächlich.
7 **obscurely** (adv.): obskur, unklar, irgendwie.
   governmental: mit der Regierung zusammenhängend.
   vaguely (adv.): auf unbestimmte Weise.
10 **chatter:** Geplapper.
11 **baby-buttock:** Baby-Pobacke.
13 **to place s.o.:** jdn. einsortieren, einschätzen.
16 **tolerable:** erträglich.
23 **pardonable:** entschuldbar.

not an easy association to make. I let curiosity guide me
between the lions, debating on the way whether I should
admit following her or pretend coincidence. In the end
I did neither, but concealed myself some tables away
5 from her in the general reading room, where she sat behind her dark glasses and a fortress of literature she'd
gathered at the desk. She sped from one book to the
next, intermittently lingering on a page, always with a
frown, as if it were printed upside down. She had a pencil
10 poised above paper – nothing seemed to catch her fancy,
still now and then, as though for the hell of it, she made
laborious scribblings. Watching her, I remembered a
girl I'd known in school, a grind, Mildred Grossman.
Mildred: with her moist hair and greasy spectacles, her
15 stained fingers that dissected frogs and carried coffee to
picket lines, her flat eyes that only turned toward the
stars to estimate their chemical tonnage. Earth and air
could not be more opposite than Mildred and Holly, yet
in my head they acquired a Siamese twinship, and the
20 thread of thought that had sewn them together ran like

2 **between the lions** (fig.): etwa: in der Höhle des Löwen.
3 **coincidence:** Zufall.
6 **fortress:** wörtl.: Festung; hier (fig.): ganzer Berg, Schutzwall.
8 **intermittently** (adv.): periodisch, abwechselnd.
   to linger on s.th.: sich bei etwas aufhalten, bei etwas verweilen.
10 **to poise:** balancieren, im Gleichgewicht halten.
11 **for the hell of it** (infml.): zum Spaß, aus Jux.
12 **laborious:** mühsam.
13 **grind:** Streber(in) (AE).
14 **greasy:** fettig.
15 **to dissect:** sezieren.
16 **picket lines:** Reihe von Streikposten (oder Demonstranten).
17 **chemical tonnage:** wörtl.: chemische Tonnage; hier vermutl.: chemi-
    sche Zusammensetzung.
19 **Siamese twinship:** siamesische Zwillingsschwesternschaft.

this: the average personality reshapes frequently, every
few years even our bodies undergo a complete overhaul –
desirable or not, it is a natural thing that we should
change. All right, here were two people who never
5   would. That is what Mildred Grossman had in common
with Holly Golightly. They would never change because
they'd been given their character too soon; which, like
sudden riches, leads to a lack of proportion: the one had
splurged herself into a top-heavy realist, the other a lop-
10 sided romantic. I imagined them in a restaurant of the
future, Mildred still studying the menu for its nutritional
values, Holly still gluttonous for everything on it. It
would never be different. They would walk through life
and out of it with the same determined step that took
15 small notice of those cliffs at the left. Such profound
observations made me forget where I was; I came to,
startled to find myself in the gloom of the library, and
surprised all over again to see Holly there. It was after
seven, she was freshening her lipstick and perking up her
20 appearance from what she deemed correct for a library to

---

1 **to reshape:** neu bilden.
2 **to undergo s.th.:** etwas unterliegen, etwas durchmachen.
   overhaul: (technische) Überholung.
9 **to splurge o.s. into s.th.:** sich in etwas (etwa: ein Vergnügen) stürzen.
   top-heavy: kopflastig.
9f. **lopsided:** einseitig.
11 **menu:** Speisekarte.
   nutritional: Nähr-.
12 **gluttonous:** unersättlich.
15 **profound:** tiefgründig.
16 **to come to:** zu sich kommen.
19 **to perk up:** verschönern, aufmöbeln.
20 **to deem:** (für etwas) halten.

what, by adding a bit of scarf, some earrings, she considered suitable for the Colony[44]. When she'd left, I wandered over to the table where her books remained; they were what I had wanted to see. *South by Thunderbird. Byways of Brazil. The Political Mind of Latin America.* And so forth.

On Christmas Eve she and Mag gave a party. Holly asked me to come early and help trim the tree. I'm still not sure how they maneuvered that tree into the apartment. The top branches were crushed against the ceiling, the lower ones spread wall-to-wall; altogether it was not unlike the yuletide giant we see in Rockefeller Plaza[45]. Moreover, it would have taken a Rockefeller to decorate it, for it soaked up baubles and tinsel like melting snow. Holly suggested she run out to Woolworth's and steal some balloons; she did: and they turned the tree into a fairly good show. We made a toast to our work, and Holly said: "Look in the bedroom. There's a present for you."

I had one for her, too: a small package in my pocket that felt even smaller when I saw, square on the bed and wrapped with a red ribbon, the beautiful bird cage.

"But, Holly! It's dreadful!"

"I couldn't agree more; but I thought you wanted it."

"The money! Three hundred and fifty dollars!"

She shrugged. "A few extra trips to the powder room.

---

4 **thunderbird:** Donnervogel (indianisches Fabelwesen).
5 **byway:** Seitenweg, Nebenstraße; auch etwa: Nebensache.
9 **to maneuver:** manövrieren.
12 **yuletide** (arch.): weihnachtlich, Weihnachts-.
14 **to soak up:** aufsaugen.
   bauble: Flitter.
   tinsel: Rauschgoldgirlande.
17 **to make a toast to s.th.:** auf etwas trinken.

Promise me, though. Promise you'll never put a living thing in it."

I started to kiss her, but she held out her hand. "Gimme," she said, tapping the bulge in my pocket.

5 "I'm afraid it isn't much," and it wasn't: a St. Christopher's medal. But at least it came from Tiffany's.

*

Holly was not a girl who could keep anything, and surely by now she has lost that medal, left it in a suitcase or some hotel drawer. But the bird cage is still mine. I've lugged
10 it to New Orleans, Nantucket[46], all over Europe, Morocco, the West Indies[47]. Yet I seldom remember that it was Holly who gave it to me, because at one point I chose to forget: we had a big falling-out, and among the objects rotating in the eye of our hurricane were the bird
15 cage and O. J. Berman and my story, a copy of which I'd given Holly when it appeared in the university review.

Sometime in February, Holly had gone on a winter trip with Rusty, Mag and José Ybarra-Jaegar. Our altercation happened soon after she returned. She was brown as
20 iodine, her hair was sun-bleached to a ghost-color, she'd had a wonderful time: "Well, first of all we were in Key West[48], and Rusty got mad at some sailors, or vice versa,

---

4 **gimme:** *give me*.
  bulge: Ausbauchung, Wölbung.
9 **to lug:** schleppen.
13 **falling-out:** Streit.
14 **to rotate:** rotieren, sich drehen.
  eye: Auge (windstilles Zentrum eines Hurrikans).
18 f. **altercation:** Auseinandersetzung.
20 **iodine:** Jod.
  sun-bleached: sonnengebleicht.
22 **vice versa:** umgekehrt.

*any*way he'll have to wear a spine brace the rest of his life.
Dearest Mag ended up in the hospital, too. First-de-
gree sunburn. Disgusting: all blisters and citronella. We
couldn't stand the smell of her. So José and I left them in
the hospital and went to Havana. He says wait till I see
Rio; but as far as I'm concerned Havana can take my
money right now. We had an irresistible guide, most of
him Negro and the rest of him Chinese, and while I don't
go much for one or the other, the combination was fairly
riveting: so I let him play kneesie under the table,
because frankly I didn't find him at all banal; but then
one night he took us to a blue movie, and what do you
suppose? There *he* was *on* the screen. Of course when we
got back to Key West, Mag was positive I'd spent the
whole time sleeping with José. So was Rusty: but he
doesn't care about that, he simply wants to hear the
details. Actually, things were pretty tense until I had a
heart-to-heart with Mag."

We were in the front room, where, though it was now
nearly March, the enormous Christmas tree, turned
brown and scentless, its balloons shriveled as an old
cow's dugs, still occupied most of the space. A recogniz-

---

1 **spine brace:** Stützapparat für das Rückgrat.
3 **blister:** Blase, Bläschen (auf der Haut).
  citronella: hier: nach Zitrone riechendes Öl zur Behandlung von Son-
  nenbrand.
10 **to play kneesie:** Knie aneinanderreiben.
12 **blue movie:** Pornofilm.
14 **to be positive:** sich sicher sein.
17 **tense:** (an)gespannt.
17 f. **to have a heart-to-heart:** sich offen aussprechen.
21 **scentless:** duftlos.
  shriveled: verschrumpelt, runzlig.
22 **dugs** (pl.): Euter.

able piece of furniture had been added to the room: an
army cot; and Holly, trying to preserve her tropic look,
was sprawled on it under a sun lamp.

"And you convinced her?"

5 "That I hadn't slept with José? God, yes. I simply told –
but you know: made it sound like an *agonized* confession
– simply told her I was a dyke."

"She couldn't have believed that."

"The hell she didn't. Why do you think she went out and
10 bought this army cot? Leave it to me: I'm always top
banana in the shock department. Be a darling, darling,
rub some oil on my back." While I was performing this
service, she said: "O. J. Berman's in town, and listen, I
gave him your story in the magazine. He was quite im-
15 pressed. Her thinks maybe you're worth helping. But he
says you're on the wrong track. Negroes and children:
who cares?"

"Not Mr. Berman, I gather."

"Well, I agree with him. I read that story twice. Brats and
20 niggers. Trembling leaves. *Description.* It doesn't *mean*
anything."

My hand, smoothing oil on her skin, seemed to have a
temper of its own: it yearned to raise itself and come
down on her buttocks. "Give me an example," I said
25 quietly. "Of something that means something. In your
opinion."

"*Wuthering Heights,*"⁴⁹ she said, without hesitation.

The urge in my hand was growing beyond control. "But

---

2 **army cot:** Feldbett (AE).
6 **agonized:** gequält.
10 f. **top banana** (slang): Oberverrückter.
20 **nigger** (pej., infml.): Nigger, Neger.
22 **to smooth:** glatt streichen, verteilen.

that's unreasonable. You're talking about a work of genius."

"It was, wasn't it? *My wild sweet Cathy*. God, I cried buckets. I saw it ten times."

5 I said, "Oh" with recognizable relief, "oh" with a shameful, rising inflection, "the *movie*."

Her muscles hardened, the touch of her was like stone warmed by the sun. "Everybody has to feel superior to somebody," she said. "But it's customary to present a

10 little proof before you take the privilege."

"I don't compare myself to you. Or Berman. Therefore I can't feel superior. We want different things."

"Don't you want to make money?"

"I haven't planned that far."

15 "That's how your stories sound. As though you'd written them without knowing the end. Well, I'll tell you: you'd better make money. You have an expensive imagination. Not many people are going to buy you bird cages."

"Sorry."

20 "You will be if you hit me. You wanted to a minute ago: I could feel it in your hand; and you want to now."

I did, terribly; my hand, my heart was shaking as I recapped the bottle of oil. "Oh no, I wouldn't regret that. I'm only sorry you wasted your money on me: Rusty

25 Trawler is too hard a way of earning it."

She sat up on the army cot, her face, her naked breasts coldly blue in the sun-lamp light. "It should take you

---

5 f. **shameful:** schändlich.
6 **inflection:** Tonfall.
9 **customary:** gebräuchlich.
17 **expensive:** kostspielig.
23 **to recap:** wieder verschließen.

about four seconds to walk from here to the door. I'll give
you two."

*

I went straight upstairs, got the bird cage, took it down
and left it in front of her door. That settled that. Or so I
imagined until the next morning when, as I was leaving
for work, I saw the cage perched on a sidewalk ashcan
waiting for the garbage collector. Rather sheepishly, I
rescued it and carried it back to my room, a capitulation
that did not lessen my resolve to put Holly Golightly
absolutely out of my life. She was, I decided, "a crude
exhibitionist," "a time waster," "an utter fake": someone never to be spoken to again.

And I didn't. Not for a long while. We passed each other
on the stairs with lowered eyes. If she walked into Joe
Bell's, I walked out. At one point, Madame Sapphia
Spanella, the coloratura and roller-skating enthusiast
who lived on the first floor, circulated a petition among
the brownstone's other tenants asking them to join her in
having Miss Golightly evicted: she was, said Madame
Spanella, "morally objectionable" and the "perpetrator

---

6 **sidewalk:** Bürgersteig, Gehweg (AE).
   ashcan (auch: *garbage can*) (AE): Mülltonne.
7 **garbage collector** (AE): Müllmann.
   sheepishly (adv.): verlegen.
9 **resolve:** Entschlossenheit.
10 **crude:** ordinär, primitiv.
11 **fake:** Schwindler(in).
16 **enthusiast:** Schwärmer(in).
17 **to circulate:** zirkulieren lassen.
   petition: Petition, Bittschrift, Gesuch.
19 **to evict:** zur Räumung zwingen.
20 **objectionable:** anstößig.
   perpetrator: Übeltäter(in); hier: jd., der ein Verbrechen begeht.

of all-night gatherings that endanger the safety and sanity of her neighbors." Though I refused to sign, secretly I felt Madame Spanella had cause to complain. But her petition failed, and as April approached May, the open-win-
5 dowed, warm spring nights were lurid with the party sounds, the loud-playing phonograph and martini laughter that emanated from Apt. 2.

It was no novelty to encounter suspicious specimens among Holly's callers, quite the contrary; but one day
10 late that spring, while passing through the brownstone's vestibule, I noticed a *very* provocative man examining her mailbox. A person in his early fifties with a hard, weathered face, gray forlorn eyes. He wore an old sweat-stained gray hat, and his cheap summer suit, a pale blue,
15 hung too loosely on his lanky frame; his shoes were brown and brand-new. He seemed to have no intention of ringing Holly's bell. Slowly, as though he were reading Braille, he kept rubbing a finger across the embossed lettering of her name.
20 That evening, on my way to supper, I saw the man again. He was standing across the street, leaning against a tree

---

1 **sanity:** Verstand, Zurechnungsfähigkeit.
5 **lurid:** gespenstisch, düster.
7 **to emanate from s.th.:** von etwas ausgehen.
8 **to encounter s.o.:** jdm. begegnen, auf jdn. stoßen.
   suspicious: verdächtig.
   specimen: Exemplar.
11 **vestibule:** Vorhalle, Foyer.
13 **forlorn:** verloren, hoffnungslos.
13f. **sweat-stained:** mit Schweißflecken bedeckt.
15 **lanky:** schmächtig, hager.
18 **Braille:** Blindenschrift.
   embossed: erhaben, geprägt.
19 **lettering:** Beschriftung, Schriftzug.

and staring up at Holly's windows. Sinister speculations
rushed through my head. Was he a detective? Or some
underworld agent connected with her Sing Sing friend,
Sally Tomato? The situation revived my tenderer feel-
5 ings for Holly; it was only fair to interrupt our feud long
enough to warn her that she was being watched. As I
walked to the corner, heading east toward the Hamburg
Heaven at Seventy-ninth and Madison[50], I could feel the
man's attention focused on me. Presently, without turn-
10 ing my head, I knew that he was following me. Because
I could hear him whistling. Not any ordinary tune, but
the plaintive, prairie melody Holly sometimes played
on her guitar: *Don't wanna sleep, don't wanna die, just
wanna go a-travelin' through the pastures of the sky.*
15 The whistling continued across Park Avenue and up
Madison. Once, while waiting for a traffic light to
change, I watched him out of the corner of my eye as
he stooped to pet a sleazy Pomeranian. "That's a fine
animal you got there," he told the owner in a hoarse,
20 countrified drawl.
Hamburg Heaven was empty. Nevertheless, he took a
seat right beside me at the long counter. He smelled of
tobacco and sweat. He ordered a cup of coffee, but when

---

1 **sinister:** unheilvoll, böse.
   speculation: Spekulation, Ahnung.
5 **feud:** Fehde.
9 **to focus:** sich konzentrieren.
12 **plaintive:** klagend.
16 **traffic light:** Ampel.
18 **to pet:** hätscheln.
   sleazy (infml.): schäbig.
   Pomeranian: Spitz (Hunderasse).
20 **countrified** (pej.): bäurisch, vom Lande.
   drawl: schleppende Sprache.

it came he didn't touch it. Instead, he chewed on a toothpick and studied me in the wall mirror facing us.

"Excuse me," I said, speaking to him via the mirror, "but
what do you want?"

5 The question didn't embarrass him; he seemed relieved
to have had it asked. "Son," he said, "I need a friend."

He brought out a wallet. It was as worn as his leathery
hands, almost falling to pieces; and so was the brittle,
cracked, blurred snapshot he handed me. There were
10 seven people in the picture, all grouped together on the
sagging porch of a stark wooden house, and all children,
except for the man himself, who had his arm around the
waist of a plump blond little girl with a hand shading her
eyes against the sun.

15 "That's me," he said, pointing at himself. "That's
her ..." he tapped the plump girl. "And this one over
here," he added, indicating a tow-headed beanpole,
"that's her brother, Fred."

I looked at "her" again: and yes, now I could see it, an
20 embryonic resemblance to Holly in the squinting, fat-
cheeked child. At the same moment, I realized who the
man must be.

---

1 f. **toothpick:** Zahnstocher.
3 **via:** über, auf dem Weg über.
7 **leathery:** ledern.
8 **brittle:** spröde, brüchig.
9 **cracked:** rissig.
   blurred: unscharf, verschwommen; befleckt.
   snapshot: Schnappschuß.
11 **stark:** schlicht.
17 **tow-headed:** flachsblond.
   beanpole: Bohnenstange.
20 **embryonic:** embryonisch, embryonal; hier: rudimentär, (noch) nicht
   voll ausgebildet.
   squinting: schielend; von der Seite schauend.

"You're Holly's *father*."

He blinked, he frowned. "Her name's not Holly. She was a Lulamae Barnes. Was," he said, shifting the toothpick in his mouth, "till she married me. I'm her husband. Doc

5 Golightly. I'm a horse doctor, animal man. Do some farming, too. Near Tulip, Texas.[51] Son, why are you laughin'?"

It wasn't real laughter; it was nerves. I took a swallow of water and choked; he pounded me on the back. "This

10 here's no humorous matter, son. I'm a tired man. I've been five years lookin' for my woman. Soon as I got that letter from Fred, saying where she was, I bought myself a ticket on the Greyhound.[52] Lulamae belongs home with her husband and her churren."

15 "Children?"

"*Them's* her churren," he said, almost shouted. He meant the four other young faces in the picture, two barefooted girls and a pair of overalled boys. Well, of course: the man was deranged. "But Holly can't be the

20 mother of those children. They're older than she is. Bigger."

"Now, son," he said in a reasoning voice, "I didn't claim they was her natural-born churren. Their own precious mother, precious woman, Jesus rest her soul, she passed

25 away July 4th, Independence Day,[53] 1936. The year of the drought. When I married Lulamae, that was in

---

5 **horse doctor** (infml.): Viehdoktor.
11 **woman** (infml.): (Ehe-)Frau, Alte.
16 **them's her churren** (dial.): *these are her children*.
18 **overalled:** mit Overall bekleidet, mit Arbeitskleidung versehen.
19 **deranged:** geistesgestört.
23 **was** (dial.): *were*.
24 f. **to pass away:** verscheiden, sterben.
26 **drought:** Dürre.

December, 1938, she was going on fourteen. Maybe an ordinary person, being only fourteen, wouldn't know their right mind. But you take Lulamae, she was an exceptional woman. She knew good-and-well what she was doing when she promised to be my wife and the mother of my churren. She plain broke our hearts when she ran off like she done." He sipped his cold coffee, and glanced at me with a searching earnestness. "Now, son, do you doubt me? Do you believe what I'm saying is so?"

I did. It was too implausible not to be fact; moreover, it dovetailed with O. J. Berman's description of the Holly he'd first encountered in California: "You don't know whether she's a hillbilly or an Okie or what." Berman couldn't be blamed for not guessing that she was a child-wife from Tulip, Texas.

"Plain broke our hearts when she ran off like she done," the horse doctor repeated. "She had no cause. All the housework was done by her daughters. Lulamae could just take it easy: fuss in front of mirrors and wash her hair. Our own cows, our own garden, chickens, pigs: son, that woman got positively fat. While her brother growed into a giant. Which is a sight different from how they come to us. 'Twas Nellie, my oldest girl, 'twas Nellie brought 'em into the house. She come to me one morn-

2f. **to know one's right mind:** wissen, was man will.
4 **good-and-well** (adv.): ganz genau.
6 **plain** (adv., infml.): schier, einfach.
7 **like she done** (dial.): *the way she did*.
   to sip: schlürfen, nippen.
11 **implausible:** unglaubwürdig, nicht plausibel.
12 **to dovetail:** übereinstimmen.
24 **come** (dial.): *came*.

ing, and said: 'Papa, I got two wild yunguns locked in the
kitchen. I caught 'em outside stealing milk and turkey
eggs.' That was Lulamae and Fred. Well, you never saw a
more pitiful something. Ribs sticking out everywhere,
5 legs so puny they can't hardly stand, teeth wobbling so
bad they can't chew mush. Story was: their mother died
of the TB, and their papa done the same – and all the
churren, a whole raft of 'em, they been sent off to live
with different mean people. Now Lulamae and her
10 brother, them two been living with some mean, no-count
people a hundred miles east of Tulip. She had good cause
to run off from that house. She didn't have none to leave
mine. 'Twas her home." He leaned his elbows on the
counter and, pressing his closed eyes with his fingertips,
15 sighed. "She plumped out to be a real pretty woman.
Lively, too. Talky as a jaybird. With something smart to
say on every subject: better than the radio. First thing
you know, I'm out picking flowers. I tamed her a crow
and taught it to say her name. I showed her how to play

1 **yunguns** (dial.): *young ones.*
2 **turkey:** Truthahn.
5 **puny** (pej.): mickrig.
  can't hardly (dial.): *can hardly* (für Dialektformen des Englischen
  typische, doppelte Verneinung).
  to wobble: wackeln.
6 **mush:** Brei.
7 **TB:** eigtl. Abk. für *Tubercle Bacillus:* Tuberkelbazillus (Erreger der
  Tuberkulose); allgem.: Tuberkulose.
  done (dial.): *1. did; 2. had done.*
8 **a whole raft of** . . .: eine ganze Menge von . . . (AE).
10 **been living** (dial.): *had been living.*
  no-count (AE, dial.): nichtsnutzig.
15 **to plump out:** Gewicht ansetzen.
16 **jaybird:** Eichelhäher.
18 **crow:** Krähe.

the guitar. Just to look at her made the tears spring to my
eyes. The night I proposed, I cried like a baby. She said:
'What you want to cry for, Doc? 'Course we'll be married. I've never been married before.' Well, I had to
5 laugh, hug and squeeze her: *never been married before!*"
He chuckled, chewed on his toothpick a moment. "Don't
tell me that woman wasn't happy!" he said, challeng-
ingly. "We all doted on her. She didn't have to lift a
finger, 'cept to eat a piece of pie. 'Cept to comb her hair
10 and send away for all the magazines. We must've had a
hunnerd dollars' worth of magazines come into that
house. Ask me, that's what done it. Looking at show-off
pictures. Reading dreams. That's what started her walking down the road. Every day she'd walk a little further: a
15 mile, and come home. Two miles, and come home. One
day she just kept on." He put his hands over his eyes
again; his breathing made a ragged noise. "The crow I
give her went wild and flew away. All summer you could
hear him. In the yard. In the garden. In the woods.
20 All summer that damned bird was calling: Lulamae,
Lulamae."
He stayed hunched over and silent, as though listening to
the long-ago summer sound. I carried our checks to the
cashier. While I was paying, he joined me. We left
25 together and walked over to Park Avenue. It was a cool,
blowy evening; swanky awnings flapped in the breeze.

---

6 **to chuckle:** kichern.
8 **to dote on s.o.:** jdn. vergöttern, abgöttisch lieben.
11 **hunnerd** (dial.): *hundred.*
12 **show-off:** Angeber-.
17 **ragged:** unregelmäßig.
26 **blowy:** windig.
  awning: Markise.
  to flap: klatschend schlagen.

The quietness between us continued until I said: "But what about her brother? He didn't leave?"

"No, sir," he said, clearing his throat. "Fred was with us right till they took him in the Army. A fine boy. Fine with
5 horses. He didn't know what got into Lulamae, how come she left her brother and husband and churren. After he was in the Army, though, Fred started hearing from her. The other day he wrote me her address. So I come to get her. I know she's sorry for what she done. I
10 know she wants to go home." He seemed to be asking me to agree with him. I told him that I thought he'd find Holly, or Lulamae, somewhat changed. "Listen, son," he said, as we reached the steps of the brownstone, "I advised you I need a friend. Because I don't want to
15 surprise her. Scare her none. That's why I've held off. Be my friend: let her know I'm here."

The notion of introducing Mrs. Golightly to her husband had its satisfying aspects; and, glancing up at her lighted windows, I hoped her friends were there, for the pros-
20 pect of watching the Texan shake hands with Mag and Rusty and José was more satisfying still. But Doc Golightly's proud earnest eyes and sweat-stained hat made me ashamed of such anticipations. He followed me into the house and prepared to wait at the bottom of the
25 stairs. "Do I look nice?" he whispered, brushing his sleeves, tightening the knot of his tie.

---

5 f. **how come** (dial.): *how it came about:* wie es kam.
9 **come** (dial.): *have come.*
  done (dial.): *has done.*
14 **to advise:** mitteilen, informieren.
15 **Scare her none:** Machen Sie ihr bloß keine Angst.
  to hold off: (sich) fernhalten.
23 **anticipation:** Erwartung.

Holly was alone. She answered the door at once; in fact, she was on her way out – white satin dancing pumps and quantities of perfume announced gala intentions. "Well, idiot," she said, and playfully slapped me with her purse. "I'm in too much of a hurry to make up now. We'll smoke the pipe tomorrow, okay?"

"Sure, Lulamae. If you're still around tomorrow."

She took off her dark glasses and squinted at me. It was as though her eyes were shattered prisms, the dots of blue and gray and green like broken bits of sparkle. "*He* told you that," she said in a small, shivering voice. "Oh, please. *Where* is he?" She ran past me into the hall. "Fred!" she called down the stairs. "Fred! Where are you, darling?"

I could hear Doc Golightly's footsteps climbing the stairs. His head appeared above the banisters, and Holly backed away from him, not as though she were frightened, but as though she were retreating into a shell of disappointment. Then he was standing in front of her, hangdog and shy. "Gosh, Lulamae," he began, and hesitated, for Holly was gazing at him vacantly, as though she couldn't place him. "Gee, honey," he said, "don't they

---

2 **pumps:** Pumps, hochhackige Damenschuhe.
4 **idiot** (infml., hum.): etwa: Spinnerchen, Doofköpfchen.
5 **to make up:** (Streit) beilegen, wiedergutmachen.
9 **shattered:** zersplittert.
   prism: (optisches) Prisma (Strahlen-, Lichtbrecher).
   dot: Tupfen.
18 **shell:** hier (fig.): Schneckenhaus.
20 **hangdog:** niedergeschlagen, zerknirscht.
   gosh (infml.): Mann!, Mensch!, Mannomann!
21 **vacantly** (adv.): (fig.) leer, abwesend.
22 **gee** (infml.): au weia, meine Güte!

feed you up here? You're so skinny. Like when I first saw you. All wild around the eye."

Holly touched his face; her fingers tested the reality of his chin, his beard stubble. "Hello, Doc," she said gently, 5 and kissed him on the cheek. "Hello, Doc," she repeated happily, as he lifted her off her feet in a rib-crushing grip. Whoops of relieved laughter shook him. "Gosh, Lulamae. Kingdom come."

Neither of them noticed me when I squeezed past them 10 and went up to my room. Nor did they seem aware of Madame Sapphia Spanella, who opened her door and yelled: "Shut up! It's a disgrace. Do your whoring elsewhere."

*

"*Divorce* him? Of course I never divorced him. I was 15 only fourteen, for God's sake. It couldn't have been *legal*." Holly tapped an empty martini glass. "Two more, my darling Mr. Bell."

Joe Bell, in whose bar we were sitting, accepted the order reluctantly. "You're rockin' the boat kinda early," he 20 complained, crunching on a Tums. It was not yet noon, according to the black mahogany clock behind the bar, and he'd already served us three rounds.

---

4 **stubble:** Stoppeln.
6 **rib-crushing:** Rippen zerquetschend.
7 **whoop:** Schrei(en), Geschrei.
8 **kingdom:** Himmel, Paradies.
9 **to squeeze:** (sich) zwängen.
12 **to yell:** gellend schreien.
 whoring: Hurerei, Herumhuren.
19 **to rock the boat** (fig.): für Unruhe sorgen.
 kinda (dial.): *kind of:* irgendwie.
22 **round:** (Getränke-)Runde.

"But it's Sunday, Mr. Bell. Clocks are slow on Sundays.
Besides, I haven't been to bed yet," she told him, and
confided to me: "Not to sleep." She blushed, and glanced
away guiltily. For the first time since I'd known her, she
seemed to feel a need to justify herself: "Well, I had to.
Doc really loves me, you know. And I love him. He may
have looked old and tacky to *you*. But you don't know
the sweetness of him, the confidence he can give to birds
and brats and fragile things like that. Anyone who ever
gave you confidence, you owe them a lot. I've always
remembered Doc in my prayers. Please stop smirking!"
she demanded, stabbing out a cigarette. "I *do* say my
prayers."
"I'm not smirking. I'm smiling. You're the most amazing
person."
"I suppose I am," she said, and her face, wan, rather
bruised-looking in the morning light, brightened; she
smoothed her tousled hair, and the colors of it glimmered
like a shampoo advertisement. "I must look fierce. But
who wouldn't? We spent the rest of the night roaming
around in a bus station. Right up till the last minute Doc
thought I was going to go with him. Even though I kept

---

3 **to confide to s.o.:** jdm. im Vertrauen mitteilen.
7 **tacky** (AE, infml.): verlottert.
9 **fragile:** zerbrechlich, zart.
11 **to smirk:** grinsen, süffisant lächeln.
12 **to stab out:** (Zigarette) ausdrücken.
16 **wan:** bleich, fahl.
17 **bruised-looking:** etwa: wie zerschlagen aussehend (*bruised:* geprellt, mit blauen Flecken).
18 **tousled:** zerzaust.
   to glimmer: schimmern.
19 **advertisement:** Reklame.
20 **to roam:** umherstreifen.

telling him: But, Doc, I'm not fourteen any more, and
I'm not Lulamae. But the terrible part is (and I realized it
while we were standing there) I am. I'm still stealing
turkey eggs and running through a brier patch. Only now
5 I call it having the mean reds."
Joe Bell disdainfully settled the fresh martinis in front of
us.

"Never love a wild thing, Mr. Bell," Holly advised him.
"That was Doc's mistake. He was always lugging home
10 wild things. A hawk with a hurt wing. One time it was a
full-grown bobcat with a broken leg. But you can't give
your heart to a wild thing: the more you do, the stronger
they get. Until they're strong enough to run into the
woods. Or fly into a tree. Then a taller tree. Then the
15 sky. That's how you'll end up, Mr. Bell. If you let yourself love a wild thing. You'll end up looking at the
sky."

"She's drunk," Joe Bell informed me.

"Moderately," Holly confessed. "But Doc knew what I
20 meant. I explained it to him very carefully, and it was
something he could understand. We shook hands and
held on to each other and he wished me luck." She
glanced at the clock. "He must be in the Blue Mountains[54] by now."

25 "What's she talkin' about?" Joe Bell asked me.

Holly lifted her martini. "Let's wish the Doc luck, too,"
she said, touching her glass against mine. "Good luck:
and believe me, dearest Doc – it's better to look at the

---

4 **brier patch:** Dornengestrüpp.
6 **disdainfully** (adv.): verächtlich, verachtungsvoll.
10 **hawk:** Falke.
11 **bobcat** (AE): Luchs.

sky than live there. Such an empty place; so vague. Just a
country where the thunder goes and things disappear."

*

TRAWLER MARRIES FOURTH. I was on a subway somewhere in Brooklyn[55] when I saw that headline. The paper
that bannered it belonged to another passenger. The
only part of the text that I could see read: *Rutherfurd*
"Rusty" Trawler, the millionaire playboy often accused of
pro-Nazi sympathies, eloped to Greenwich[56] yesterday
with a beautiful – Not that I wanted to read any more.
Holly had married him: well, well. I wished I were under
the wheels of the train. But I'd been wishing that before I
spotted the headline. For a headful of reasons. I hadn't
seen Holly, not really, since our drunken Sunday at Joe
Bell's bar. The intervening weeks had given me my own
case of the mean reds. First off, I'd been fired from my
job: deservedly, and for an amusing misdemeanor too
complicated to recount here. Also, my draft board was
displaying an uncomfortable interest; and, having so
recently escaped the regimentation of a small town, the
idea of entering another form of disciplined life made me
desperate. Between the uncertainty of my draft status

---

3 **subway:** U-Bahn (AE).
4 **headline:** Schlagzeile.
5 **to banner s.th.:** etwas mit Schlagzeilen melden.
8 **to elope:** durchbrennen, ausreißen.
12 **to spot:** entdecken.
15 **first off** (infml.): zunächst.
16 **deservedly** (adv.): verdientermaßen.
   misdemeanor: Fehlverhalten.
17 **to recount:** (genauer) erzählen.
   draft board: Einberufungsbehörde, Wehrerfassungsbehörde.
19 **regimentation:** Reglementierung.

and a lack of specific experience, I couldn't seem to find
another job. That was what I was doing on a subway in
Brooklyn: returning from a discouraging interview with
an editor of the now defunct newspaper, *P M*⁵⁷. All this,
combined with the city heat of the summer, had reduced
me to a state of nervous inertia. So I more than half
meant it when I wished I were under the wheels of the
train. The headline made the desire quite positive. If
Holly could marry that "absurd foetus," then the army of
wrongness rampant in the world might as well march
over me. Or, and the question is apparent, was my outrage a little the result of being in love with Holly myself?
A little. For I *was* in love with her. Just as I'd once been in
love with my mother's elderly colored cook and a postman who let me follow him on his rounds and a whole
family named McKendrick. That category of love gener-
ates jealousy, too.

When I reached my station I bought a paper; and, reading the tail-end of that sentence, discovered that Rusty's
bride was: *a beautiful cover girl from the Arkansas hills,
Miss Margaret Thatcher Fitzhue Wildwood*. Mag! My
legs went so limp with relief I took a taxi the rest of the
way home.

Madame Sapphia Spanella met me in the hall, wild-eyed

---

1 **specific:** eigen, besonder(e, -er, -es), bestimmt.
4 **defunct:** eingestellt, nicht mehr erscheinend.
6 **inertia:** Trägheit.
9 **foetus:** Fetus (ungeborenes Kind vom dritten Schwangerschaftsmo-
    nat an).
10 **rampant:** wuchernd, im Schwange.
11 f. **outrage:** hier: Empörung, Entrüstung.
19 **tail-end:** hinteres Ende.
22 **limp:** schlaff.
24 **wild-eyed:** wild blickend.

and wringing her hands. "Run," she said. "Bring the police. She is killing somebody! Somebody is killing her!"

It sounded like it. As though tigers were loose in Holly's apartment. A riot of crashing glass, of rippings and fallings and overturned furniture. But there were no quarreling voices inside the uproar, which made it seem unnatural. "Run," shrieked Madame Spanella, pushing me. "Tell the police murder!"

I ran; but only upstairs to Holly's door. Pounding on it had one result: the racket subsided. Stopped altogether. But pleadings to let me in went unanswered, and my efforts to break down the door merely culminated in a bruised shoulder. Then below I heard Madame Spanella commanding some newcomer to go for the police. "Shut up," she was told, "and get out of my way."

It was José Ybarra-Jaegar. Looking not at all the smart Brazilian diplomat; but sweaty and frightened. He ordered me out of his way, too. And, using his own key, opened the door. "In here, Dr. Goldman," he said, beckoning to a man accompanying him.

Since no one prevented me, I followed them into the apartment, which was tremendously wrecked. At last the

---

1 **to wring one's hands:** die Hände ringen.
5 **riot:** Getöse, Krawall.
  to rip: reißen.
6 **to overturn:** umwerfen.
7 **uproar:** Tumult.
11 **racket:** Krach.
  to subside: sich legen, verstummen.
12 **pleading:** dringende Bitte.
13 **to culminate:** gipfeln, enden.
20f. **to beckon:** (zu)winken.
23 **wrecked:** kurz und klein geschlagen, zerstört.

Christmas tree had been dismantled, very literally: its brown dry branches sprawled in a welter of torn-up books, broken lamps and phonograph records. Even the icebox had been emptied, its contents tossed around the room: raw eggs were sliding down the walls, and in the midst of the debris Holly's no-name cat was calmly licking a puddle of milk.

In the bedroom, the smell of smashed perfume bottles made me gag. I stepped on Holly's dark glasses; they were lying on the floor, the lenses already shattered, the frames cracked in half.

Perhaps that is why Holly, a rigid figure on the bed, stared at José so blindly, seemed not to see the doctor, who, testing her pulse, crooned: "You're a tired young lady. Very tired. You want to go to sleep, don't you? Sleep."

Holly rubbed her forehead, leaving a smear of blood from a cut finger. "Sleep," she said, and whimpered like an exhausted, fretful child. "He's the only one would ever let me. Let me hug him on cold nights. I saw a place in Mexico. With horses. By the sea."

"With horses by the sea," lullabied the doctor, selecting from his black case a hypodermic.

---

1 **to dismantle:** demontieren; hier: abschmücken.
2 **welter:** Wirrwarr.
4 **icebox** (AE): Eisschrank.
6 **debris:** Trümmer.
7 **puddle:** Pfütze, Lache.
9 **to gag:** würgen, übel werden (AE).
14 **to croon:** leise und beruhigend sprechen.
18 **to whimper:** wimmern.
19 **fretful:** reizbar.
22 **to lullaby:** ein Wiegenlied singen.
23 **hypodermic:** (Injektions-)Spritze.

José averted his face, queasy at the sight of a needle. "Her sickness is only grief?" he asked, his difficult English lending the question an unintended irony. "She is grieving only?"

5 "Didn't hurt a bit, now did it?" inquired the doctor, smugly dabbing Holly's arm with a scrap of cotton. She came to sufficiently to focus the doctor. "*Everything* hurts. Where are my glasses?" But she didn't need them. Her eyes were closing of their own accord.

10 "She is only grieving?" insisted José.

"Please, sir," the doctor was quite short with him, "if you will leave me alone with the patient."

José withdrew to the front room, where he released his temper on the snooping, tiptoeing presence of Madame

15 Spanella. "Don't touch me! I'll call the police," she threatened as he whipped her to the door with Portuguese oaths.

He considered throwing me out, too; or so I surmised from his expression. Instead, he invited me to have a

20 drink. The only unbroken bottle we could find contained dry vermouth. "I have a worry," he confided. "I have a worry that this should cause scandal. Her crashing every-

---

1 **to avert:** abwenden.
  queasy: übel, Übelkeit empfindend.
3 **unintended:** unabsichtlich.
6 **smugly** (adv.): hier: selbstzufrieden.
  to dab: tupfen.
  scrap: Fetzen, Stückchen.
9 **of one's own accord:** freiwillig.
13 **to release:** hier: freien Lauf lassen.
14 **to snoop:** (herum)schnüffeln, spionieren.
  to tiptoe: auf Zehenspitzen gehen.
18 **to surmise:** argwöhnen.

thing. Conducting like a crazy. I must have no public scandal. It is too delicate: my name, my work."

He seemed cheered to learn that I saw no reason for a "scandal"; demolishing one's own possessions was, pre-
5 sumably, a private affair.

"It is only a question of grieving," he firmly declared. "When the sadness came, first she throws the drink she is drinking. The bottle. Those books. A lamp. Then I am scared. I hurry to bring a doctor."

10 "But why?" I wanted to know. "Why should she have a fit over Rusty? If I were her, I'd celebrate."

"Rusty?"

I was still carrying my newspaper, and showed him the headline.

15 "Oh, that." He grinned rather scornfully. "They do us a grand favor, Rusty and Mag. We laugh over it: how they think they break our hearts when all the time we *want* them to run away. I assure you, we were laughing when the sadness came." His eyes searched the litter on the
20 floor; he picked up a ball of yellow paper. "This," he said.

It was a telegram from Tulip, Texas: *Received notice young Fred killed in action overseas stop your husband*

---

1 **to conduct:** *to conduct o.s.:* sich aufführen.
  crazy: hier: Verrückte(r).
2 **delicate:** delikat, heikel.
4 **to demolish:** zerstören.
4f. **presumably** (adv.): vermutlich.
11 **fit:** Anfall.
15 **to grin:** grinsen.
  scornfully (adv.): verächtlich.
19 **litter:** Abfall, Wust.
23 **in action:** im Kampf, im Gefecht.

*and children join in the sorrow of our mutual loss stop
letter follows love Doc.*

*

Holly never mentioned her brother again: except once.
Moreover, she stopped calling me Fred. June, July, all
through the warm months she hibernated like a winter
animal who did not know spring had come and gone. Her
hair darkened, she put on weight. She became rather
careless about her clothes: used to rush round to the
delicatessen wearing a rain-slicker and nothing underneath. José moved into the apartment, his name replac-
ing Mag Wildwood's on the mailbox. Still, Holly was a
good deal alone, for José stayed in Washington three
days a week. During his absences she entertained no one
and seldom left the apartment – except on Thursdays,
when she made her weekly trip to Ossining.
Which is not to imply that she had lost interest in life; far
from it, she seemed more content, altogether happier
than I'd ever seen her. A keen sudden un-Holly-like
enthusiasm for homemaking resulted in several un-
Holly-like purchases: at a Parke-Bernet[58] auction she
acquired a stag-at-bay hunting tapestry and, from the
William Randolph Hearst[59] estate, a gloomy pair of
Gothic "easy" chairs; she bought the complete Modern

---

5 **to hibernate:** überwintern.
9 **rain-slicker** (AE): gelber Regenmantel.
13 **to entertain:** hier: bewirten.
16 **to imply:** bedeuten, einschließen, (auf etwas) schließen lassen.
19 **homemaking** (AE): Hausfrauenhaftes, -tätigkeit.
21 **stag-at-bay:** (von Hunden) gestellter Hirsch.
   tapestry: Wandteppich.
23 **Gothic:** neogotisch; (fig.) vorsintflutlich.

Library[60], shelves of classical records, innumerable Metropolitan Museum[61] reproductions (including a statue of a Chinese cat that her own cat hated and hissed at and ultimately broke), a Waring[62] mixer and a pressure cooker and a library of cook books. She spent whole hausfrau afternoons slopping about in the sweatbox of her midget kitchen: "José says I'm better than the Colony. Really, who would have dreamed I had such a great natural talent? A month ago I couldn't scramble eggs."
And still couldn't, for that matter. Simple dishes, steak, a proper salad, were beyond her. Instead, she fed José, and occasionally myself, *outré* soups (brandied black terrapin poured into avocado shells) Nero-ish[63] novelties (roasted pheasant stuffed with pomegranates and persimmons) and other dubious innovations (chicken and saffron rice served with a chocolate sauce: "An East Indian classic, *my* dear.") Wartime sugar and cream

---

1 **innumerable:** zahllos.
2 **reproduction:** (Kunst-)Druck.
4 **ultimately** (adv.): schließlich.
4f. **pressure cooker:** Dampfkochtopf.
6 **to slop about** (infml.): herumschlurfen.
   sweatbox: Glühofen, Brutkasten.
7 **midget kitchen:** Zwergenküche, Mini-Küche.
9 **to scramble eggs:** Rühreier machen.
10 **for that matter:** eigentlich.
12 **outré, e** (Fr.): ausgefallen, ganz extravagant.
   to brandy: mit Branntwein anrichten, übergießen.
12f. **terrapin:** nordamerikanische Sumpfschildkröte.
14 **pheasant:** Fasan.
   pomegranate: Granatapfel.
14f. **persimmon:** Persimone (orangefarbene, eßbare Beere).
15 **dubious:** dubios, zweifelhaft.
   innovation: Neuerung.
16 **saffron:** Safran.

rationing restricted her imagination when it came to sweets – nevertheless, she once managed something called Tobacco Tapioca: best not describe it.

Nor describe her attempts to master Portuguese, an ordeal as tedious to me as it was to her, for whenever I visited her an album of Linguaphone[64] records never ceased rotating on the phonograph. Now, too, she rarely spoke a sentence that did not begin, "After we're married –" or "When we move to Rio –" Yet José had never suggested marriage. She admitted it. "But, after all, he *knows* I'm preggers. Well, I am, darling. Six weeks gone. I don't see why *that* should surprise you. It didn't me. Not *un peu* bit. I'm delighted. I want to have at least nine. I'm sure some of them will be rather dark – José has a touch of *le nègre*, I suppose you guessed that? Which is fine by me: what could be prettier than a quite coony baby with bright green beautiful eyes? I wish, please don't laugh – but I wish I'd been a virgin for him, for José. Not that I've warmed the multitudes some people say: I don't blame the bastards for *saying* it, I've always thrown out such a

---

1 **rationing:** Rationierung.
　to restrict: beschränken, Zügel anlegen.
3 **tapioca:** Tapioka (aus den Wurzelknollen des Maniokstrauchs gewonnenes Stärkeprodukt); hier: Gericht unter Verwendung von Tapioka.
5 **ordeal:** Prüfung, Mühsal.
　tedious: öde, langweilig, lästig.
11 **preggers** (BE, infml.): *pregnant:* schwanger.
　six weeks gone: hier: schon sechs Wochen (drüber).
13 **un peu** (Fr.): ein wenig.
15 **le nègre** (Fr.): der Neger.
16 **coony** (pej.): niggerähnlich.
20f. **to throw out a jazzy line:** etwas ganz Verrücktes äußern, etwas ganz Wildes andeuten.

jazzy line. Really, though, I toted up the other night, and I've only had eleven lovers – not counting anything that happened before I was thirteen because, after all, that just *doesn't* count. Eleven. Does that make me a whore?
Look at Mag Wildwood. Or Honey Tucker. Or Rose Ellen Ward. They've had the old clap-yo'-hands so many times it amounts to applause. Of course I haven't anything *against* whores. Except this: some of them may have an honest tongue but they all have dishonest hearts.
I mean, you can't bang the guy and cash his checks and at least not *try* to believe you love him. I never have. Even Benny Shacklett and all those rodents. I sort of hypnotized myself into thinking their sheer rattiness had a certain allure. Actually, except for Doc, if you want to count Doc, José is my first non-rat romance. Oh, he's not my idea of the absolute finito. He tells little lies and he worries what people *think* and he takes about fifty baths a day: men ought to smell *some*what. He's too prim, too cautious to be my guy ideal; he always turns his back to get undressed and he makes too much noise when he eats and I don't like to see him run because there's something funny-looking about him when he runs. If I were free

---

1 **to tote up:** aufaddieren, zusammenzählen.
4 **whore:** Hure.
6 **clap-yo'-hands:** Wortspiel mit *to clap one's hands* ›in die Hände klatschen‹ und *clap* (slang) ›Tripper‹.
10 **to bang** (slang, vulg.): ‚bumsen'.
12 **rodent:** Nagetier.
13 **sheer:** wahrhaftig, rein, bar.
   rattiness: Rattenähnlichkeit.
14 **allure:** Verlockung, Reiz.
16 **finito** (Ital.): hier etwa: Ideal, Vollkommenheit, Endgültiges.
18 **prim:** geziert.

to choose from everybody alive, just snap my fingers
and say come here you. I wouldn't pick José. Nehru[65],
he's nearer the mark. Wendell Willkie.[66] I'd settle for
Garbo[67] any day. Why not? A person ought to be able to
marry men or women or – listen, if you came to me and
said you wanted to hitch up with Man o' War, I'd respect
your feeling. No, I'm serious. Love should be allowed.
I'm all for it. Now that I've got a pretty good idea what it
is. Because I *do* love José – I'd stop smoking if he asked
me to. He's *friendly*, he can laugh me out of the mean
reds, only I don't have them much any more, except
sometimes, and even then they're not so hideola that I
gulp Seconal or have to haul myself to Tiffany's: I take
his suit to the cleaner, or stuff some mushrooms, and I
feel fine, just great. Another thing, I've thrown away my
horoscopes. I must have spent a dollar on every goddamn
star in the goddamn planetarium. It's a bore, but the
answer is good things only happen to you if you're good.
Good? Honest is more what I mean. Not law-type honest
– I'd rob a grave, I'd steal two-bits off a dead man's eyes if
I thought it would contribute to the day's enjoyment –
but unto-thyself-type honest. Be anything but a coward,

---

6 **to hitch up with s.o.:** (fig.) mit jdm. anspannen.
  Man o' War: eigtl.: Kriegsschiff; hier vermutl.: Portugiese (von *Portuguese Man-of-War* ›portugiesische Galeere‹).
12 **hideola:** *hideous:* scheußlich, schrecklich.
13 **to gulp:** (gierig) schlucken.
  to haul: schleppen.
14 **mushroom:** Pilz.
17 **bore** (infml.): Last, Plage.
19 **law-type:** etwa: dem Buchstaben des Gesetzes nach.
20 **two-bits** (AE): 25-Cent-Stücke (mit denen gelegentlich die Augen von Toten bedeckt werden); auch (fig.): Kinkerlitzchen, Kleinigkeit.
22 **unto-thyself-type:** sich selbst (treu) gegenüber.

a pretender, an emotional crook, a whore: I'd rather
have cancer than a dishonest heart. Which isn't being
pious. Just practical. Cancer *may* cool you, but the
other's sure to. Oh, screw it, cookie – hand me my guitar
5 and I'll sing you a *fada* in *the* most perfect Portuguese."
Those final weeks, spanning end of summer and the
beginning of another autumn, are blurred in memory,
perhaps because our understanding of each other had
reached that sweet depth where two people communi-
10 cate more often in silence than in words: an affectionate
quietness replaces the tensions, the unrelaxed chatter
and chasing about that produce a friendship's more
showy, more, in the surface sense, dramatic moments.
Frequently, when *he* was out of town (I'd developed hos-
15 tile attitudes toward *him*, and seldom used his name)
we spent entire evenings together during which we
exchanged less than a hundred words; once, we walked
all the way to Chinatown, ate a chow-mein supper,
bought some paper lanterns and stole a box of joss sticks,
20 then moseyed across the Brooklyn Bridge[68], and on the
bridge, as we watched seaward-moving ships pass be-

---

1 **pretender:** jd., der (ungerechtfertigte) Ansprüche erhebt.
  crook (infml.): Gauner.
2 **cancer:** Krebs (Krankheit).
4 **screw it** (slang): hier: laß sein, hör auf damit.
  cookie (AE, infml.): Typ, Knabe.
5 **fada** (Port.): *fado:* portugiesisches Volkslied in klagendem Ton.
11 **tension:** Spannung.
12 **to chase about:** sich herumtreiben.
13 **showy:** auffallend, auffällig, prahlerisch, großspurig.
18 **chow-mein:** chinesisch-amerikanisches Gericht aus Pilzen, Fleisch,
  Krabben usw., mit gebratenen Nudeln serviert.
19 **joss stick:** Räucherstäbchen.
20 **to mosey** (AE, slang): schlendern, bummeln.

tween the cliffs of burning skyline, she said: "Years from now, years and years, one of those ships will bring me back, me and my nine Brazilian brats. Because yes, they *must* see this, these lights, the river – I love New York, even though it isn't mine, the way something has to be, a tree or a street or a house, something, anyway, that belongs to me because I belong to it." And I said: "Do shut up," for I felt infuriatingly left out – a tugboat in dry-dock while she, glittery voyager of secure destination, steamed down the harbor with whistles whistling and confetti in the air.

So the days, the last days, blow about in memory, hazy, autumnal, all alike as leaves: until a day unlike any other I've lived.

*

It happened to fall on the 30th of September, my birthday, a fact which had no effect on events, except that, expecting some form of monetary remembrance from my family, I was eager for the postman's morning visit. Indeed, I went downstairs and waited for him. If I had not been loitering in the vestibule, then Holly would not have asked me to go horse-back riding; and would not, consequently, have had the opportunity to save my life.

"Come on," she said, when she found me awaiting the

---

8 **infuriatingly** (adv.): aufreizend, rasend machend.
  tugboat: Schlepper, Schleppkahn.
8 f. **dry-dock:** Trockendock.
9 **destination:** Bestimmungs-, Zielort.
12 **hazy:** verschwommen, dunstig.
17 **monetary:** geldlich.
20 **to loiter:** herumlungern, herumtrödeln.

postman. "Let's walk a couple of horses around the park." She was wearing a windbreaker and a pair of blue jeans and tennis shoes; she slapped her stomach, drawing attention to its flatness: "Don't think I'm out to lose the
5 heir. But there's a horse, my darling old Mabel Minerva – I can't go without saying good-bye to Mabel Minerva."

"Good-bye?"

"A week from Saturday. José bought the tickets." In rather a trance, I let her lead me down to the street. "We
10 change planes in Miami. Then over the sea. Over the Andes. Taxi!"

Over the Andes. As we rode in a cab across Central Park it seemed to me as though I, too, were flying, desolately floating over snow-peaked and perilous territory.

15 "But you can't. After all, what about. Well, what about. Well, you can't *really* run off and leave everybody."

"I don't think anyone will miss me. I have no friends."

"I will. Miss you. So will Joe Bell. And oh – millions. Like Sally. Poor Mr. Tomato."

20 "I loved old Sally," she said, and sighed. "You know I haven't been to see him in a month? When I told him I was going away, he was an angel. *Actually*"– she frowned – "he seemed *delighted* that I was leaving the country. He said it was all for the best. Because sooner or later
25 there might be trouble. If they found out I wasn't his real niece. That fat lawyer, O'Shaughnessy, sent me

---

2 **windbreaker** (AE): Windjacke.
9 **trance:** Trance, Traum.
11 **Andes:** Anden (südamerikanische Bergkette an der Pazifikküste).
13 **desolately** (adv.): verlassen, einsam.
14 **snow-peaked:** mit schneebedeckten Gipfeln.
  perilous: gefährlich.
15 **what about:** etwa: und was ist mit (mir)?

five hundred dollars. In cash. A wedding present from Sally."

I wanted to be unkind. "You can expect a present from me, too. When, and if, the wedding happens."

5 She laughed. "He'll marry me, all right. In church. And with his family there. That's why we're waiting till we get to Rio."

"Does he know you're married already?"

"What's the matter with you? Are you trying to ruin the 10 day? It's a beautiful day: leave it alone!"

"But it's perfectly possible –"

"It *isn't* possible. I've told you, that wasn't legal. It *couldn't* be." She rubbed her nose, and glanced at me sideways. "Mention that to a living soul, darling. I'll hang 15 you by your toes and dress you for a hog."

The stables – I believe they have been replaced by television studios – were on West Sixty-sixth street.[69] Holly selected for me an old sway-back black and white mare: "Don't worry, she's safer than a cradle." Which, in my 20 case, was a necessary guarantee, for ten-cent pony rides at childhood carnivals were the limit of my equestrian experience. Holly helped hoist me into the saddle, then mounted her own horse, a silvery animal that took the

---

14 **sideways:** von der Seite.
15 **to dress s.o. for a hog** (fig.): jdn. als Spanferkel garnieren, zurechtma-
chen (*hog:* Schwein).
18 **sway-back:** Schaukelrücken.
   mare: Stute.
19 **cradle:** Wiege.
20 **guarantee:** Garantie.
21 **carnival:** Volksfest.
   equestrian: reiterlich.
22 **to hoist:** hochheben, hieven.

lead as we jogged across the traffic of Central Park West and entered a riding path dappled with leaves denuding breezes danced about.

"See?" she shouted. "It's great!"

5 And suddenly it was. Suddenly, watching the tangled colors of Holly's hair flash in the red-yellow leaf light, I loved her enough to forget myself, my self-pitying despairs, and be content that something she thought happy was going to happen. Very gently the horses began
10 to trot, waves of wind splashed us, spanked our faces, we plunged in and out of sun and shadow pools, and joy, a glad-to-be-alive exhilaration, jolted through me like a jigger of nitrogen. That was one minute; the next introduced farce in grim disguise.

15 For all at once, like savage members of a jungle ambush, a band of Negro boys leapt out of the shrubbery along the path. Hooting, cursing, they launched rocks and thrashed at the horse's rumps with switches.

Mine, the black and white mare, rose on her hind legs,

1 **to jog:** trotten, traben.
2 **dappled:** gesprenkelt.
  to denude: entblößen.
3 **to dance s.th. about:** etwas herumwirbeln.
10 **to splash:** bespritzen.
  to spank: klapsen.
12 **exhilaration:** Hochgefühl.
  to jolt: durchzucken.
13 **nitrogen:** Stickstoff.
15 **ambush:** Hinterhalt.
16 **shrubbery:** Buschwerk, Gebüsch.
17 **to hoot:** rufen, schreien.
  to launch: schleudern.
18 **to thrash:** prügeln, dreschen.
  rump: Rumpf, Rücken.
  switch: Gerte.
19 **hind leg:** Hinterbein, Hinterhand.

whinnied, teetered like a tightrope artist, then blue-
streaked down the path, bouncing my feet out of the
stirrups and leaving me scarcely attached. Her hooves
made the gravel stones spit sparks. The sky careened.
Trees, a lake with little-boy sailboats, statues went by
licketysplit. Nursemaids rushed to rescue their charges
from our awesome approach; men, bums and others,
yelled: "Pull in the reins!" and "Whoa, boy, whoa!" and
"Jump!" It was only later that I remembered these voices; at the time I was simply conscious of Holly, the
cowboy-sound of her racing behind me, never quite
catching up, and over and over calling encouragements.
Onward: across the park and out into Fifth Avenue:
stampeding against the noonday traffic, taxis, buses that
screechingly swerved. Past the Duke mansion, the Frick
Museum, past the Pierre and the Plaza.[70] But Holly

---

1 **to whinny:** wiehern.
  to teeter: schaukeln, schwanken.
  tightrope: Drahtseil.
1f. **to blue-streak:** etwa: wie ein geölter Blitz rasen.
2 **to bounce:** stoßen.
3 **stirrup:** Steigbügel.
  attached: hier: fest (im Sattel) sitzend.
  hoof: Huf.
4 **gravel:** Kies.
  to careen: krängen, sich auf die Seite legen.
6 **licketysplit** (AE, adv.): blitzschnell, mit Volldampf.
  nursemaid: Kindermädchen.
  charge: hier: Schützling.
7 **awesome:** Furcht einflößend.
8 **rein:** Zügel.
  whoa: brr! (Kommando zum Anhalten von Pferden).
12 **to catch up:** auf-, einholen.
14 **to stampede:** (in Panik) losstürmen.
15 **to screech:** quietschen.
  to swerve: seitlich ausweichen.

gained ground; moreover, a mounted policeman had joined the chase: flanking my runaway mare, one on either side, their horses performed a pincer movement that brought her to a steamy halt. It was then, at last, that I fell off her back. Fell off and picked myself up and stood there, not altogether certain where I was. A crowd gathered. The policeman huffed and wrote in a book: presently he was most sympathetic, grinned and said he would arrange for our horses to be returned to their stable.

Holly put us in a taxi. "Darling. How do you feel?"

"Fine."

"But you haven't *any* pulse," she said, feeling my wrist.

"Then I must be dead."

"No, idiot. This is serious. Look at me."

The trouble was, I couldn't see her; rather, I saw several Holly's, a trio of sweaty faces so white with concern that I was both touched and embarrassed. "Honestly. I don't feel anything. Except ashamed."

"Please. Are you sure? Tell me the truth. You might have been killed."

"But I wasn't. And thank you. For saving my life. You're wonderful. Unique. I love you."

"Damn fool." She kissed me on the cheek. Then there were four of her, and I fainted dead away.

*

1 **to gain ground:** Boden gewinnen, aufholen.
  mounted: beritten.
2 **runaway:** durchgegangen (Pferd).
3 **pincer movement:** Zangenbewegung.
7 **to huff:** beleidigt, eingeschnappt sein.
23 **unique:** einzigartig.
25 **dead** (adv.): komplett, völlig.

That evening, photographs of Holly were frontpaged by
the late edition of the *Journal-American* and by the early
editions of both the *Daily News* and the *Daily Mirror*.[71]
The publicity had nothing to do with runaway horses.
5 It concerned quite another matter, as the headlines
revealed: PLAYGIRL ARRESTED IN NARCOTICS SCANDAL
(Journal-American), ARREST DOPE-SMUGGLING ACTRESS
(Daily News), DRUG RING EXPOSED, GLAMOUR GIRL
HELD *(Daily Mirror)*.
10 Of the lot, the *News* printed the most striking picture:
Holly, entering police headquarters, wedged between
two muscular detectives, one male, one female. In this
squalid context even her clothes (she was still wearing
her riding costume, windbreaker and blue jeans) sug-
15 gested a gang-moll hooligan: an impression dark glasses,
disarrayed coiffure and a Picayune cigarette dangling
from sullen lips did not diminish. The caption read:

---

1 **to be frontpaged:** auf der Titelseite abgedruckt sein.
6 **narcotics** (pl.): Rauschgift.
7 **dope-smuggling:** Stoffschmuggeln (*dope* [infml.]: ‚Stoff‘, Droge[n]).
8 **drug:** Droge, Rauschgift.
   exposed: entlarvt, aufgeflogen.
   glamour girl: Glamourgirl (Mädchen, das nur für Vergnügungen im
   Kreis der oberen Zehntausend lebt).
10 **of the lot:** von diesen (allen).
11 **headquarters** (pl.): Hauptquartier.
   to wedge: einzwängen.
12 **muscular:** muskulös.
13 **squalid:** (fig.) schmutzig.
15 **gang-moll** (slang): Gangsterbraut.
   hooligan: Rowdy.
16 **disarrayed:** derangiert, unordentlich.
   coiffure: Haarfrisur.
   to dangle: hängen, baumeln (lassen).
17 **sullen:** mürrisch, verdrossen.
   caption: Bildunterschrift.

Twenty-year-old Holly Golightly, beautiful movie starlet and café society celebrity D. A. alleges to be key figure in international drug-smuggling racket linked to racketeer Salvatore "Sally" Tomato. Dets. Patrick Connor and
5 *Sheilah Fezzonetti (L. and R.) are shown escorting her into 67th St. Precinct. See story on Pg. 3.* The story, featuring a photograph of a man identified as Oliver "Father" O'Shaughnessy (shielding his face with a fedora), ran three full columns. Here, somewhat con-
10 densed, are the pertinent paragraphs: *Members of café society were stunned today by the arrest of gorgeous Holly Golightly, twenty-year-old Hollywood starlet and highly publicized girl-about-New York. At the same time, 2 P. M., police nabbed Oliver O'Shaughnessy, 52, of the Hotel*

1 **starlet:** Sternchen.
2 **café society:** Besucher von (teuren) Cafés.
   D. A.: Abk. für *District Attorney:* Staatsanwalt (AE).
   to allege: vorwerfen.
3 **racket:** (kriminelles) Geschäft.
   racketeer: Geschäftemacher, Gauner.
4 **Dets.:** Abk. für *Detectives:* Kriminalpolizisten.
5 **to escort:** eskortieren, geleiten.
6 **precinct:** Polizeirevier (AE).
7 **to feature:** darstellen, zeigen.
8 **Father:** Anrede katholischer Geistlicher: Hochwürden.
8f. **fedora:** weicher Filzhut (oft mit seitlich und hinten hochgebogener Krempe).
9f. **to condense:** ver-, abkürzen.
10 **pertinent:** relevant.
11 **to be stunned:** wie betäubt, fassungslos sein.
    gorgeous: hinreißend.
13 **publicized:** in den Zeitungen (groß) herausgebracht.
    girl-about-New York: etwa: leichtlebiges Mädchen in New York (vgl. *man-about-town:* Lebemann).
14 **to nab** (infml.): erwischen, schnappen.

Seabord, W. 49th St.,[72] *as he exited from a Hamburg*
Heaven on Madison Ave. Both are alleged by District
Attorney Frank L. Donovan to be important figures in an
international drug ring dominated by the notorious Mafia-
führer[73] *Salvatore "Sally" Tomato, currently in Sing Sing*
serving a five-year rap for political bribery ... O'Shaugh-
nessy, a defrocked priest variously known in crimeland
circles as "Father" and "The Padre," has a history of
arrests dating back to 1934, when he served two years for
operating a phony Rhode Island mental institution, The
Monastery. Miss Golightly, who has no previous crim-
inal record, was arrested in her luxurious apartment at a
swank East Side address. ... Although the D. A.'s office
has issued no formal statement, responsible sources
insist the blond and beautiful actress, not long ago
the constant companion of multimillionaire Rutherfurd
Trawler, has been acting as "liaison" between the impris-
oned Tomato and his chief-lieutenant, O'Shaughnessy.
... Posing as a relative of Tomato's, Miss Golightly is said

1 **to exit:** hinausgehen.
4 **to dominate:** beherrschen.
 notorious: berüchtigt.
6 **rap:** Gefängnisstrafe.
 bribery: Bestechung.
7 **defrocked:** aus dem Priesteramt verstoßen.
 crimeland: Unterwelt.
8 **Padre** (Ital.): Anrede für Priester: Hochwürden.
10 **phony:** unecht, falsch.
11 **monastery:** Kloster.
11f. **to have no previous criminal record:** nicht vorbestraft sein.
12 **luxurious:** luxuriös, elegant.
13 **swank:** *swanky.*
17 **liaison:** V-Mann, Verbindungsmann.
18 **chief-lieutenant:** etwa: Hauptstatthalter.
19 **to pose as s.o.:** als jd. auftreten, sich als jd. ausgeben.

to have paid weekly visits to Sing Sing, and on these occasions Tomato supplied her with verbally coded messages which she then transmitted to O'Shaughnessy. Via this link, Tomato, believed to have been born in Cefalù, Sicily,[74] in 1874, was able to keep first-hand control of a world-wide narcotics syndicate with outposts in Mexico, Cuba, Sicily, Tangier, Tehran and Dakar. But the D. A.'s office refused to offer any detail on these allegations or even verify them. ... Tipped off, a large number of reporters were on hand at the E. 67th St. Precinct station when the accused pair arrived for booking. O'Shaughnessy, a burly red-haired man, refused comment and kicked one cameraman in the groin. But Miss Golightly, a fragile eyeful, even though attired like a tomboy in slacks and leather jacket, appeared relatively unconcerned. "Don't ask me what the hell this is about," she told reporters. "Parce-que je ne sais pas, mes chères. (Because I do not

    2 **coded:** kodiert, verschlüsselt.
    5 **first-hand:** aus erster Hand, direkt, unmittelbar.
    6 **outpost:** Vorposten.
    7 **Tangier:** Tanger (Hafenstadt in Marokko).
    8 **allegation:** Behauptung.
    9 **to verify:** bestätigen.
       to tip off: einen Hinweis geben.
  10 **on hand:** zur Hand, zugegen.
  11 **booking:** hier: Aufnahme der Personalien und des zur Last gelegten Vergehens eines Festgenommenen.
  12 **burly:** kräftig, stämmig.
  13 **groin:** Leiste(ngegend), Unterleib (besonders in bezug auf männliche Geschlechtsteile gebraucht).
  14 **eyeful** (infml.): schöner Anblick.
      even though: obwohl, selbst wenn.
      attired: gekleidet.
      tomboy: richtiger Junge, Wildfang.
      slacks (pl.): lange Hose.

*know, my dears). Yes – I have visited Sally Tomato. I used
to go to see him every week. What's wrong with that? He
believes in God, and so do I."* ... Then, under the subheading ADMITS OWN DRUG ADDICTION: *Miss Golightly*
5 *smiled when a reporter asked whether or not she herself is
a narcotics user. "I've had a little go at marijuana. It's not
half so destructive as brandy. Cheaper, too. Unfortu-
nately, I prefer brandy. No, Mr. Tomato never mentioned
drugs to me. It makes me furious, the way these wretched
10 people keep persecuting him. He's a sensitive, a religious
person. A darling old man."*

There is one especially gross error in this report: she was
not arrested in her "luxurious apartment." It took place
in my own bathroom. I was soaking away my horse-ride
15 pains in a tub of scalding water laced with Epsom salts;
Holly, an attentive nurse, was sitting on the edge of the
tub waiting to rub me with Sloan's liniment and tuck me
into bed. There was a knock at the front door. As the
door was unlocked, Holly called Come in. In came
20 Madame Sapphia Spanella, trailed by a pair of civilian-

---

3 f. **subheading:** Untertitel.
4 **drug addiction:** Drogenabhängigkeit.
6 **to have a go at s.th.:** es mal mit etwas versuchen.
7 **destructive:** verderblich, zerstörerisch.
10 **to persecute:** drangsalieren, verfolgen.
12 **gross:** grob.
14 **to soak away:** hier: durch Einweichen auflösen.
15 **tub:** Badewanne.
 to scald: brühen, kochen.
 laced with: mit einem Schuß ...
 Epsom salts (pl.): Bittersalz.
17 **liniment:** Einreibemittel.
20 **to trail:** auf der Spur folgen.
20 f. **civilian-clothed:** in Zivil.

clothed detectives, one of them a lady with thick yellow
braids roped round her head.
"*Here* she is: the wanted woman!" boomed Madame
Spanella, invading the bathroom and leveling a finger,
first at Holly's, then my nakedness. "Look. What a
whore she is." The male detective seemed embarrassed:
by Madame Spanella and by the situation; but a harsh
enjoyment tensed the face of his companion – she
plumped a hand on Holly's shoulder and, in a surprising
baby-child voice, said: "Come along, sister. You're
going places." Whereupon Holly coolly told her: "Get
them cotton-pickin' hands off of me, you dreary, drivel-
ing old bull-dyke." Which rather enraged the lady: she
slapped Holly damned hard. So hard, her head twisted
on her neck, and the bottle of liniment, flung from her
hand, smithereened on the tile floor – where I, scamper-
ing out of the tub to enrich the fray, stepped on it and all
but severed both big toes. Nude and bleeding a path of

---

2 **braid:** Flechte, Zopf (AE).
3 **to boom:** dröhnen.
4 f. **to level at s.th.:** auf etwas zielen, richten.
8 **to tense:** anspannen.
9 **to plump:** etwa (schwer) fallen lassen.
11 **to go places:** einen Ausflug machen.
12 **them** (dial.): *those.*
   dreary: trübe.
12 f. **to drivel** (pej.): labern, faseln.
13 **to enrage:** wütend machen.
16 **to smithereen:** in tausend Scherben zerspringen.
   tile: Fliese.
16 f. **to scamper:** flitzen, huschen.
17 **to enrich:** an-, bereichern.
   fray: Schlägerei; hier: Schlachtfeld.
18 **to sever:** abtrennen.
   nude: nackt.

bloody footprints, I followed the action as far as the hall. "Don't forget," Holly managed to instruct me as the detectives propelled her down the stairs, "please feed the cat."

*

5   Of course I believed Madame Spanella to blame: she'd several times called the authorities to complain about Holly. It didn't occur to me the affair could have dire dimensions until that evening when Joe Bell showed up flourishing the newspapers. He was too agitated to speak
10 sensibly; he caroused the room hitting his fists together while I read the accounts.

Then he said: "You think it's so? She was mixed up in this lousy business?"

"Well, yes."

15 He popped a Tums in his mouth and, glaring at me, chewed it as though he were crunching my bones. "Boy, that's rotten. And you meant to be her friend. What a bastard!"

"Just a minute. I didn't say she was involved *knowingly*.
20 She wasn't. But there, she did do it. Carry messages and whatnot –"

He said: "Take it pretty calm, don't you? Jesus, she could get ten years. More." He yanked the papers away from

---

1 **footprint**: Fußspur.
3 **to propel**: vorwärtstreiben.
7 **dire**: schrecklich.
9 **to flourish**: schwenken.
10 **to carouse**: hier etwa: (durchs Zimmer) toben.
13 **lousy** (slang): saumäßig, lausig.
15 **to pop**: stopfen, stecken.
17 **rotten**: lausig, verkommen.
23 **to yank**: reißen.

me. "You know her friends. These rich fellows. Come down to the bar, we'll start phoning. Our girl's going to need fancier shysters than I can afford."

I was too sore and shaky to dress myself; Joe Bell had to
5 help. Back at his bar he propped me in the telephone booth with a triple martini and a brandy tumbler full of coins. But I couldn't think who to contact. José was in Washington, and I had no notion where to reach him there. Rusty Trawler? Not that bastard! Only: what
10 other friends of hers did I know? Perhaps she'd been right when she'd said she had none, not really.

I put through a call to Crestview 5-6958 in Beverly Hills[75], the number long-distance information gave me for O. J. Berman. The person who answered said Mr.
15 Berman was having a massage and couldn't be disturbed: sorry, try later. Joe Bell was incensed – told me I should have said it was a life and death matter; and he insisted on my trying Rusty. First, I spoke to Mr. Trawler's butler – Mr. and Mrs. Trawler, he announced, were at dinner
20 and might he take a message? Joe Bell shouted into the receiver: "This is urgent, mister. Life and death." The outcome was that I found myself talking – listening, rather – to the former Mag Wildwood: "Are you

---

3 **fancy:** toll, schick.
  shyster (AE, slang): Rechtsverdreher.
5 **to prop s.o.:** jdn. setzen.
5f. **telephone booth:** Telefonkabine.
6 **triple:** dreifach.
  tumbler: (Wasser-)Glas.
13 **long-distance information:** Fernsprechauskunft.
16 **incensed:** aufgebracht, wütend.
21 **urgent:** dringend.
  mister (infml.): Anrede.
22 **outcome:** Folge, Ergebnis.

114

starkers?" she demanded. "My husband and I will positively *sue* anyone who attempts to connect our names
with that ro-ro-ro*vol*ting and de-de-de*gen*-erate girl. I
always *knew* she was a hop-hop-head with no more mor-
als than a hound-bitch in heat. Prison is where she
belongs. And my husband agrees one thousand percent.
We will positively *sue* anyone who –" Hanging up, I remembered old Doc down in Tulip, Texas; but no, Holly
wouldn't like it if I called him, she'd kill me good.

I rang California again; the circuits were busy, stayed
busy, and by the time O. J. Berman was on the line I'd
emptied so many martinis he had to tell me why I was
phoning him: "About the kid, is it? I know already. I
spoke already to Iggy Fitelstein. Iggy's the best shingle in
New York. I said Iggy you take care of it, send me the
bill, only keep my name anonymous, see. Well, I owe the
kid something. Not that I owe her *any*thing, you want to
come down to it. She's crazy. A phony. But a *real* phony,
you know? Anyway, they only got her in ten thousand
bail. Don't worry, Iggy'll spring her tonight – it wouldn't
surprise me she's home already."

*

  1 **starkers:** Kurzform von *stark mad:* völlig verrückt.
  3 **rovolting:** *revolting:* abscheulich, widerlich.
  4 **hophead** (AE, slang): Fixer.
  5 **hound-bitch in heat:** läufige Hündin.
  9 **good** (adv.): schön, richtig.
 10 **circuit:** hier: (Telefon-)Leitung.
 11 **on the line:** am Apparat.
 14 **shingle** (AE, infml.): (fig.) Schild, Adresse.
 17 f. **you want to come down to it:** wenn man's genau nimmt.
 20 **bail:** *on bail:* gegen Kaution.
    to spring s.o. (infml.): jdn. (aus dem Gefängnis) ‚rausholen‘.

But she wasn't; nor had she returned the next morning when I went down to feed her cat. Having no key to the apartment, I used the fire escape and gained entrance through a window. The cat was in the bedroom, and he
5 was not alone: a man was there, crouching over a suitcase. The two of us, each thinking the other a burglar, exchanged uncomfortable stares as I stepped through the window. He had a pretty face, lacquered hair, he resembled José; moreover, the suitcase he'd been packing con-
10 tained the wardrobe José kept at Holly's, the shoes and suits she fussed over, was always carting to menders and cleaners. And I said, certain it was so: "Did Mr. Ybarra-Jaegar send you?"

"I am the cousin," he said with a wary grin and just-
15 penetrable accent.

"Where is José?"

He repeated the question, as though translating it into another language. "Ah, *where* she is! She is waiting," he said and, seeming to dismiss me, resumed his valet
20 activities.

So: the diplomat was planning a powder. Well, I wasn't amazed; or in the slightest sorry. Still, what a heartbreaking stunt: "He ought to be horse-whipped."

The cousin giggled, I'm sure he understood me. He shut

---

5 **to crouch:** sich bücken.
6 **burglar:** Einbrecher.
7 **stare:** starrer Blick.
8 **to lacquer:** (mit Haarspray) fixieren.
11 **to cart** (infml.): (mit sich) schleppen.
14 **wary:** vorsichtig.
14 f. **just-penetrable:** gerade eben verständlich.
19 **valet:** Kammerdiener.
21 **to plan a powder** (AE, slang): sich aus dem Staub machen wollen.
23 **stunt:** Kunststück, Nummer.

the suitcase and produced a letter. "My cousin, she ask
me leave that for his chum. You will oblige?"
On the envelope was scribbled: *For Miss H. Golightly –
Courtesy Bearer.*

I sat down on Holly's bed, and hugged Holly's cat to me,
and felt as badly for Holly, every iota, as she could feel
for herself.

"Yes, I will oblige."

*

And I did: without the least wanting to. But I hadn't the
courage to destroy the letter; or the will power to keep it
in my pocket when Holly very tentatively inquired if, if
by any chance, I'd had news of José. It was two mornings
later; I was sitting by her bedside in a room that reeked of
iodine and bedpans, a hospital room. She had been there
since the night of her arrest. "Well, darling," she'd
greeted me, as I tiptoed toward her carrying a carton of
Picayune cigarettes and a wheel of new-autumn violets,
"I lost the heir." She looked not quite twelve years: her
pale vanilla hair brushed back, her eyes, for once minus
their dark glasses, clear as rain water – one couldn't
believe how ill she'd been.
Yet it was true: "Christ, I nearly cooled. No fooling,

---

2 **chum** (infml.): Kumpel.
4 **courtesy bearer:** hier: durch den Überbringer.
6 **iota:** Jota, Kleinigkeit.
11 **tentatively** (adv.): vorsichtig, unverbindlich.
13 **to reek of s.th.:** nach etwas riechen.
14 **bedpan:** Bettpfanne.
16 **carton:** Stange (Zigaretten).
17 **wheel** (AE, slang): Dollar; hier: Strauß (für einen Dollar).
19 **vanilla:** vanillefarben.
22 **to cool** (slang): *to be cooled:* umgebracht werden.

the fat woman almost had me. She was yakking up a
storm. I guess I couldn't have told you about the fat
woman. Since I didn't know about her myself until
my brother died. Right away I was wondering where
5 he'd gone, what it meant, Fred's dying; and then I
saw her, she was there in the room with me, and she
had Fred cradled in her arms, a fat mean red bitch
rocking in a rocking chair with Fred on her lap and
laughing like a brass band. The mockery of it! But it's
10 all that's ahead for us, my friend: this comedienne
waiting to give you the old razz. Now do you see why
I went crazy and broke everything?"
Except for the lawyer O. J. Berman had hired, I was the
only visitor she had been allowed. Her room was shared
15 by other patients, a trio of triplet-like ladies who,
examining me with an interest not unkind but total,
speculated in whispered Italian. Holly explained that:
"They think you're my downfall, darling. The fellow
what done me wrong"; and, to a suggestion that she set
20 them straight, replied: "I can't. They don't speak Eng-

---

1 **the fat woman almost had me** (slang): die Dicke hätte mich beinahe
fertiggemacht.
to yak up (slang): herbeiquatschen.
7 **to cradle:** (in den Armen) wiegen.
bitch (pej.): blöde Kuh, Miststück.
9 **brass band:** Blasorchester.
the mockery of it: welch ein Hohn.
10 **comedienne:** Komödiantin, Komikerin.
11 **to give s.o. the old razz:** jdn. verhohnepiepeln, sich über jdn. lustig
machen.
15 **triplet-like:** drillingähnlich.
18 **downfall:** Ruin.
19 **what done** (dial.): *who did.*
19f. **to set s.o. straight:** jdn. (über die Wahrheit) aufklären.

lish. Anyway, I wouldn't dream of spoiling their fun." It
was then that she asked about José.

The instant she saw the letter she squinted her eyes and
bent her lips in a tough tiny smile that advanced her age
immeasurably. "Darling," she instructed me, "would
you reach in the drawer there and give me my purse. A
girl doesn't read this sort of thing without her lipstick."

Guided by a compact mirror, she powdered, painted
every vestige of twelve-year-old out of her face. She
shaped her lips with one tube, colored her cheeks from
another. She penciled the rims of her eyes, blued the lids,
sprinkled her neck with 4711; attached pearls to her ears
and donned her dark glasses; thus armored, and after a
displeased appraisal of her manicure's shabby condition,
she ripped open the letter and let her eyes race through it
while her stony small smile grew smaller and harder.
Eventually she asked for a Picayune. Took a puff:
"Tastes bum. But divine," she said and, tossing me the
letter: "Maybe this will come in handy – if you ever write

3 **to squint one's eyes:** die Augen zusammenkneifen.
5 **immeasurably** (adv.): unermeßlich, grenzenlos.
8 **compact mirror:** Spiegel in der Puderdose.
9 **vestige:** (fig.) Spur.
11 **to pencil:** hier: Lidstrich ziehen.
   rim: Rand.
   lid: (Augen-)Lid.
12 **to sprinkle:** besprühen.
13 **to don:** aufsetzen, anziehen.
   armored: gewappnet.
14 **appraisal:** Begutachtung, Taxierung.
   manicure: Maniküre.
   shabby: schäbig.
18 **bum** (infml.): beschissen.
19 **to come in handy:** sehr gelegen kommen.

a rat-romance. Don't be hoggy: read it aloud. I'd like to hear it myself."

It began: "My dearest little girl –"

Holly at once interrupted. She wanted to know what I
5 thought of the handwriting. I thought nothing: a tight, highly legible, uneccentric script. "It's him to a T. Buttoned up and constipated," she declared. "Go on."

"My dearest little girl, I have loved you knowing you were not as others. But conceive of my despair upon
10 discovering in such a brutal and public style how very different you are from the manner of woman a man of my faith and career could hope to make his wife. Verily I grief for the disgrace of your present circumstance, and do not find it in my heart to add my condemn to the
15 condemn that surrounds you. So I hope you will find it in your heart not to condemn me. I have my family to protect, and my name, and I am a coward where those institutions enter. Forget me, beautiful child. I am no longer here. I am gone home. But may God always be
20 with you and your child. May God be not the same as – José."

"Well?"

"In a way it seems quite honest. And even touching."

"*Touching?* That square-ball jazz!"

---

1 **rat-romance:** etwa: Miesling-Romanze.
  to be hoggy: etwa: fies sein, alles für sich allein in Anspruch nehmen.
6 **legible:** lesbar.
  it's him to a T: das ist er, wie er leibt und lebt.
6f. **buttoned up:** (fig.) zugeknöpft (d. h. immer korrekt).
7 **constipated:** träge.
12 **verily** (adv.): wahrlich.
13 **to grief:** *to grieve.*
14 **condemn:** *condemnation.*
24 **square-ball jazz** (slang): etwa: Spießergewäsch.

120

"But after all, he *says* he's a coward; and from his point of view, you must see –"

Holly, however, did not want to admit that she saw; yet her face, despite its cosmetic disguise, confessed it.

5 "All right, he's not a rat without reason. A super-sized, King Kong-type[76] rat like Rusty. Benny Shacklett. But oh gee, golly goddamn," she said, jamming a fist into her mouth like a bawling baby, "I *did* love him. The rat."

10 The Italian trio imagined a lover's *crise* and, placing the blame for Holly's groanings where they felt it belonged, tut-tutted their tongues at me. I was flattered: proud that anyone should think Holly cared for me. She quieted when I offered her another cigarette. She swallowed and

15 said: "Bless you, Buster. And bless you for being such a bad jockey. If I hadn't had to play Calamity Jane I'd still be looking forward to the grub in an unwed mama's home. Strenuous exercise, that's what did the trick. But I've scared *la merde* out of the whole badge-department

20 by saying it was because Miss Dykeroo slapped me. Yes-

---

7 **golly** (infml.): Mensch(enskind)!

8 **to bawl:** brüllen.

10 **crise** (Fr.): Krise.

12 **to tut-tut:** mit der Zunge klicken.

15 **buster** (AE, infml.): Meister (Anrede).

16 **Calamity Jane:** Pechmarie.

17 **grub:** hier (fig.): Würmchen.

17 f. **unwed mamas' home:** Heim für ledige Mütter.

18 **strenuous:** anstrengend.
   to do the trick (infml.): hier: klappen lassen, zuwege bringen.

19 **to scare la merde out of s.o.** (infml.): jdn. so erschrecken, daß er sich vor Angst (fast) in die Hosen macht.
   badge-department: etwa: Dienstmarkenabteilung.

20 **Miss Dykeroo:** etwa: Fräulein Oberlesbe.

sir, I can sue them on several counts, including false arrest."

Until then, we'd skirted mention of her more sinister tribulations, and this jesting reference to them seemed
5 appalling, pathetic, so definitely did it reveal how incapable she was of recognizing the bleak realities before her. "Now, Holly," I said, thinking: be strong, mature, an uncle. "Now, Holly. We can't treat it as a joke. We have to make plans."

10 "You're too young to be stuffy. Too small. By the way, what business is it of yours?"

"None. Except you're my friend, and I'm worried. I mean to know what you intend doing."

She rubbed her nose, and concentrated on the ceiling.
15 "Today's Wednesday, isn't it? So I suppose I'll sleep until Saturday, really get a good *schluffen*. Saturday morning I'll skip out to the bank. Then I'll stop by the apartment and pick up a nightgown or two and my Mainbocher. Following which, I'll report to Idlewild[77].
20 Where, as you damn well know, I have a perfectly fine reservation on a perfectly fine plane. And since you're

---

1 **count:** Anklagepunkt.
3 **to skirt:** umgehen, vermeiden.
4 **tribulation:** Sorge, Kummer.
  jesting: scherzhaft.
5 **appalling:** erschreckend.
  pathetic: mitleiderregend.
6 **bleak:** düster, finster.
7 **mature:** reif, erwachsen.
10 **stuffy:** spießig, zimperlich, öde.
16 **schluffen** (Yid.): richtig: schlof: Schlaf.
17 **to skip:** hüpfen, springen.
18 **nightgown:** Nachthemd.
19 **Mainbocher:** vermutl. Markenname für einen Regenmantel.

such a friend I'll let you wave me off. *Please* stop shaking
your head."

"Holly. Holly. You can't do that."

"*Et pourquoi pas*? I'm not hot-footing after José, if that's
what you suppose. According to my census, he's strictly a
citizen of Limboville. It's only: Why should I waste a
perfectly fine ticket? Already paid for? Besides, I've
never been to Brazil."

"Just what kind of pills have they been feeding you here?
Can't you realize, you're under a criminal indictment. If
they catch you jumping bail, they'll throw away the key.
Even if you get away with it, you'll never be able to come
home."

"Well, so, tough titty. Anyway, home is where you feel at
home. I'm still looking."

"No, Holly, it's stupid. You're innocent. You've go to
stick it out."

She said, "Rah, team, rah," and blew smoke in my face.
She was impressed, however; her eyes were dilated by
unhappy visions, as were mine: iron rooms, steel cor-

---

4 **Et pourquoi pas?** (Fr.): Und warum nicht?
   to hot-foot after s.o.: jdm. schleunigst folgen, hinterherlaufen.
5 **census:** Schätzung.
6 **Limboville:** fiktiver Städtename (*limbo:* Vorhölle, Ort für Uner-
   wünschte).
10 **indictment:** Anklage.
11 **to jump bail** (infml.): abhauen (während man auf Kaution freigelas-
   sen ist).
   to throw away the key (fig): etwa: lange einlochen.
12 **to get away with s.th.:** bei etwas nicht erwischt werden.
14 **tough titty** (AE, slang): Pech.
17 **to stick s.th. out** (infml.): etwas durchstehen.
18 **rah** (AE, infml.): Kurzform von *hurrah*.
   team: Gespann.
19 **to dilate:** weit werden (Augen).

ridors of gradually closing doors. "Oh, screw it," she said, and stabbed out her cigarette. "I have a fair chance they *won't* catch me. Provided *you* keep your *bouche fermée*. Look. Don't despise me, darling." She put her
5 hand over mine and pressed it with sudden immense sincerity. "I haven't much choice. I talked it over with the lawyer: oh, I didn't tell *him* anything *re* Rio – he'd tip the badgers himself, rather than lose his fee, to say nothing of the nickels O. J. put up for bail. Bless O. J.'s heart; but
10 once on the coast I helped him win more than ten thou in a single poker hand: we're square. No, here's the real shake: all the badgers want from me is a couple of free grabs and my services as a state's witness against Sally – nobody has any intention of prosecuting me, they
15 haven't a ghost of a case. Well, I may be rotten to the core, Maude, *but*: testify against a friend I will not. Not if they can prove he doped Sister Kenny. My yardstick is

---

3 **bouche** (Fr.): Mund.
4 **fermé, e** (Fr.): geschlossen.
5 f. **sincerity:** Aufrichtigkeit.
7 **re:** Abk. für *regarding:* bezüglich.
8 **badgers:** Polizisten (wörtl.: Dienstmarkenträger).
   fee: Honorar.
9 **nickel:** Fünfcentstück (AE).
10 **thou:** Kurzform von *thousand*.
11 **poker hand:** Poker-Blatt.
   to be square: quitt sein.
13 **grab:** hier: Grabscher.
   state's witness: Kronzeuge.
14 **to prosecute:** gerichtlich verfolgen.
15 **not a ghost of a case:** nicht den Hauch, nicht die Spur eines Falls.
15 f. **to the core:** durch und durch.
16 **Maude:** Mädchenname.
   to testify: (vor Gericht) aussagen.
17 **Sister:** (Kranken-, Ordens-)Schwester (Anrede).
   yardstick: Meßlatte, Maßstab.

how somebody treats me, and old Sally, all right he
wasn't absolutely white with me, say he took a slight
advantage, just the same Sally's an okay shooter, and I'd
let the fat woman snatch me sooner than help the law-
boys pin him down." Tilting her compact mirror above
her face, smoothing her lipstick with a crooked pinkie,
she said: "And to be honest, that isn't all. Certain shades
of limelight wreck a girl's complexion. Even if a jury gave
me the Purple Heart, this neighborhood holds no future:
they'd still have up every rope from LaRue to Perona's
Bar and Grill[78] – take my word, I'd be about as welcome
as Mr. Frank E. Campbell[79]. And if you lived off my
particular talents, Cookie, you'd understand the kind of
bankruptcy I'm describing. Uh, uh, I don't just fancy a
fade-out that finds me belly-bumping around Roseland[80]
with a pack of West Side hillbillies. While the excellent
Madame Trawler sashayes her twat in and out of Tiffany's. I couldn't take it. Give me the fat woman any
day."

---

2 **to be white with s.o.:** mit jdm. offen sein.
3 **okay shooter:** etwa: richtiger Würfler (der keine falschen Würfel
benutzt); hier (fig.): ehrlicher Spieler.
4f. **law-boys** (slang, pej.): Jungs von der Polente.
6 **pinkie** (AE, infml.): kleiner Finger.
8 **limelight:** Rampenlicht.
jury: Jury, Ausschuß; die Geschworenen.
9 **Purple Heart:** Verwundetenabzeichen für amerikanische Soldaten.
10 **to have up a rope:** hier: ein Seil (zum Lynchen) aufhängen.
14 **bankruptcy:** Bankrott, Konkurs.
15 **fade-out:** Ausblenden; hier: Abgang.
to belly-bump (AE, infml.): eine Bauchlandung machen.
16 **pack:** Horde, Meute.
17 **to sashaye s.th.** (AE, infml.): etwas (tänzelnd) bewegen.
twat (vulg.): hier: Saftarsch.

A nurse, soft-shoeing into the room, advised that visiting hours were over. Holly started to complain, and was curtailed by having a thermometer popped in her mouth. But as I took leave, she unstoppered herself to say: "Do me a favor, darling. Call up the *Times*, or whatever you call, and get a list of the fifty richest men in Brazil. I'm *not* kidding. The fifty richest: regardles of race or color. Another favor – poke around my apartment till you find that medal you gave me. The St. Christopher. I'll need it for the trip."

*

The sky was red Friday night, it thundered, and Saturday, departing day, the city swayed in a squall-like downpour. Sharks might have swum through the air, though it seemed improbable a plane could penetrate it.

But Holly, ignoring my cheerful conviction that her flight would not go, continued her preparations – placing, I must say, the chief burden of them on me. For she had decided it would be unwise of her to come near the brownstone. Quite rightly, too: it was under surveillance, whether by police or reporters or other interested parties one couldn't tell – simply a man, sometimes men, who hung around the stoop. So she'd gone from the hospital to a bank and straight then to Joe Bell's bar. "She

---

1 **to soft-shoe:** auf leisen Sohlen kommen.
3 **to curtail:** abkürzen.
4 **to unstopper:** Stopfen entfernen.
7 **to kid:** Witze machen.
8 **to poke around s.th.** (infml.): etwas durchwühlen.
13 **shark:** Hai.
14 **to penetrate:** durchdringen.
19 f. **surveillance:** Überwachung.
22 **stoop:** Treppe (AE).

don't figure she was followed," Joe Bell told me when he
came with a message that Holly wanted me to meet her
there as soon as possible, a half-hour at most, bringing:
"Her jewelry. Her guitar. Toothbrushes and stuff. And a
bottle of hundred-year-old brandy: she says you'll find it
hid down in the bottom of the dirty-clothes basket. Yeah,
oh, and the cat. She wants the cat. But hell," he said, "I
don't know we should help her at all. She ought to be
protected against herself. Me, I feel like telling the cops.
Maybe if I go back and build her some drinks, maybe I
can get her drunk enough to call it off."

Stumbling, skidding up and down the fire escape between Holly's apartment and mine, wind-blown and
winded and wet to the bone (clawed to the bone as well,
for the cat had not looked favorably upon evacuation,
especially in such inclement weather) I managed a fast,
first-rate job of assembling her going-away belongings. I
even found the St. Christopher's medal. Everything was
piled on the floor of my room, a poignant pyramid of
brassières and dancing slippers and pretty things I
packed in Holly's only suitcase. There was a mass left
over that I had to put in paper grocery bags. I couldn't
think how to carry the cat; until I thought of stuffing him
in a pillowcase.

---

1 **don't** (dial.): *doesn't*.
9 **cop** (pej.): ‚Bulle‘, ‚Polyp‘.
14 **winded:** außer Atem.
 to claw: (mit Klauen) kratzen.
15 **evacuation:** Evakuierung, Aussiedlung.
16 **inclement:** unfreundlich (Wetter).
19 **poignant:** schmerzlich, ergreifend.
20 **brassière:** Büstenhalter.
 dancing slipper: Tanzschuh.
22 **grocery bag:** Einkaufstüte.
24 **pillowcase:** Kopfkissen(bezug).

Never mind why, but once I walked from New Orleans to
Nancy's Landing[81], Mississippi, just under five hundred
miles. It was a light-hearted lark compared to the jour-
ney to Joe Bell's bar. The guitar filled with rain, rain
5 softened the paper sacks, the sacks split and perfume
spilled on the pavement, pearls rolled in the gutter: while
the wind pushed and the cat scratched, the cat screamed
– but worse, I was frightened, a coward to equal José:
those storming streets seemed aswarm with unseen pres-
10 ences waiting to trap, imprison me for aiding an outlaw.
The outlaw said: "You're late, Buster. Did you bring the
brandy?"
And the cat, released, leaped and perched on her shoul-
15 der: his tail swung like a baton conducting rhapsodic
music. Holly, too, seemed inhabited by melody, some
bouncy *bon voyage* oompahpah. Uncorking the brandy,
she said: "This was meant to be part of my hope chest.
The idea was, every anniversary we'd have a swig. Thank
20 Jesus I never bought the chest. Mr. Bell, sir, three
glasses."

3 **lark** (infml.): Jux, Spaß.
6 **gutter:** Gosse.
9 (*to be*) **aswarm with s.th.:** voll von etwas sein, von etwas wimmeln.
10 f. **to aid an outlaw:** einem Geächteten helfen, einem Gesetzesbrecher
Beihilfe leisten.
15 **baton:** Taktstock.
to conduct: dirigieren.
17 **bouncy:** vergnügt, munter.
bon voyage (Fr.): gute Reise.
oompahpah: lautmalerisch für Musik mit Pauken und Trommeln:
Rumtata.
18 **hope chest** (AE): Aussteuertruhe.
19 **anniversary:** *wedding anniversary:* Hochzeitstag.
swig: Schluck.

"You'll only need two," he told her. "I won't drink to your foolishness."

The more she cajoled him ("Ah, Mr. Bell. The lady doesn't vanish every day. Won't you toast her?"), the gruffer he was: "I'll have no part of it. If you're going to hell, you'll go on your own. With no further help from me." An inaccurate statement: because seconds after he'd made it a chauffeured limousine drew up outside the bar, and Holly, the first to notice it, put down her brandy, arched her eyebrows, as though she expected to see the District Attorney himself alight. So did I. And when I saw Joe Bell blush, I had to think: by God, he *did* call the police. But then, with burning ears, he announced: "It's nothing. One of them Carey Cadillacs.[82] I hired it. To take you to the airport."

He turned his back on us to fiddle with one of his flower arrangements. Holly said: "Kind, dear Mr. Bell. Look at me, sir."

He wouldn't. He wrenched the flowers from the vase and thrust them at her; they missed their mark, scattered on the floor. "Good-bye," he said; and, as though he were going to vomit, scurried to the men's room. We heard the door lock.

---

3 **to cajole s.o.:** jdm. gut zureden.
4 **to toast s.o.:** auf jds. Wohl trinken.
5 **gruff:** mürrisch, barsch.
8 **to draw up:** vorfahren, anhalten.
10 **to arch one's eyebrows:** die Augenbrauen hochziehen.
11 **to alight:** aussteigen.
16 **to fiddle with s.th.:** an etwas herumspielen.
19 **to wrench:** reißen.
22 **to vomit:** sich erbrechen.
   to scurry: eilen, hasten.
   men's room: Herrentoilette.

The Carey chauffeur was a worldly specimen who accepted our slapdash luggage most civilly and remained rock-faced when, as the limousine swished uptown through a lessening rain, Holly stripped off her clothes, the riding costume she'd never had a chance to substitute, and struggled into a slim black dress. We didn't talk: talk could have only led to argument; and also, Holly seemed too preoccupied for conversation. She hummed to herself, swigged brandy, she leaned constantly forward to peer out the windows, as if she were hunting an address – or, I decided, taking a last impression of a scene she wanted to remember. It was neither of these. But this: "Stop here," she ordered the driver, and we pulled to the curb of a street in Spanish Harlem[83]. A savage, a garish, a moody neighborhood garlanded with poster-portraits of movie stars and Madonnas. Sidewalk litterings of fruit-rind and rotted newspaper were hurled about by the wind, for the wind still boomed, though the

---

1 **worldly:** (rein) materiell orientiert.
2 **slapdash:** schludrig, schlampig.
3 **rock-faced:** ungerührt, keine Miene verziehend.
  to swish: rauschen, sausen, schwirren.
  uptown: in den nordwestlichen Teil von Manhattan (etwa von der Höhe des Central Park an).
8 **preoccupied:** in Gedanken verloren.
9 **to swig** (infml.): (in großen Schlucken) trinken.
10 **to peer:** schauen, gucken.
14 **curb:** Straßenrand, Bordstein.
15 **garish:** grell, knallig.
  moody: launenhaft, launisch; verdrießlich.
  garlanded: geschmückt.
16 **poster-portrait:** Plakatporträt.
17 **fruit-rind:** Obstschale, Schale von Früchten.
  to hurl: schleudern.

rain had hushed and there were bursts of blue in the sky.

Holly stepped out of the car; she took the cat with her. Cradling him, she scratched his head and asked. "What do you think? This ought to be the right kind of place for a tough guy like you. Garbage cans. Rats galore. Plenty of cat-bums to gang around with. So scram," she said, dropping him; and when he did not move away, instead raised his thug-face and questioned her with yellowish pirate-eyes, she stamped her foot: "I said beat it!" He rubbed against her leg. "I said fuck off!" she shouted, then jumped back in the car, slammed the door, and: "Go," she told the driver. "Go. Go."

I was stunned. "Well, you *are*. You *are* a bitch."

We'd traveled a block before she replied. "I told you. We just met by the river one day: that's all. Independents, both of us. We never made each other any promises. We never –" she said, and her voice collapsed, a tic, an invalid whiteness seized her face. The car had paused for a traffic light. Then she had the door open, she was running down the street; and I ran after her.

But the cat was not at the corner where he'd been left.

---

1 **burst:** hier: Aufblitzen, Riß.
4 **to scratch:** hier: kraulen.
6 **galore:** in Hülle und Fülle, im Überfluß.
7 **cat-bum:** streunende Katze.
  to gang around with s.o.: sich mit jdm. herumtreiben.
  to scram (infml.): abhauen, verschwinden.
9 **thug-face:** Gesicht eines Schläger(typs).
10 **beat it** (infml.): hau ab.
11 **fuck off** (vulg.): verpiß dich.
18 **to collapse:** zusammenbrechen; hier: stocken, versagen.
  tic: Zucken.
19 **invalid:** kränklich.

There was no one, nothing on the street except a urinating drunk and two Negro nuns herding a file of sweet-singing children. Other children emerged from doorways and ladies leaned over their window sills to watch as
5 Holly darted up and down the block, ran back and forth chanting: "You. Cat. Where are you? Here, cat." She kept it up until a bumpy-skinned boy came forward dangling an old tom by the scruff of its neck: "You wants a nice kitty, miss? Gimme a dollar."
10 The limousine had followed us. Now Holly let me steer her toward it. At the door, she hesitated; she looked past me, past the boy still offering his cat ("Halfa dollar. Two-bits, maybe? Two-bits, it ain't much"), and she shuddered, she had to grip my arm to stand up: "Oh, Jesus
15 God. We did belong to each other. He was mine."
Then I made her a promise, I said I'd come back and find her cat: "I'll take care of him, too. I promise."
She smiled: that cheerless new pinch of a smile. "But what about me?" she said, whispered, and shivered
20 again. "I'm very scared, Buster. Yes, at last. Because it could go on forever. Not knowing what's yours until you've thrown it away. The mean reds, they're nothing.

---

1 f. **to urinate:** urinieren.
2 **to herd:** hüten.
3 **to emerge:** auftauchen.
4 **window sill:** Fensterbrett.
5 **to dart:** stürzen, schnell laufen.
6 **to chant:** (in gleichen Abständen wiederholt) rufen.
7 **bumpy-skinned:** mit rauher Haut, mit grobporiger Haut.
8 **by the scruff of its neck:** am Genick.
   you wants: *do you want.*
9 **kitty** (infml.): Mieze(katze).
12 **halfa:** *half a* (die Schreibweise deutet einen spanischen Akzent an).
18 **pinch:** winzige Kleinigkeit, Prise.

The fat woman, she nothing. This, though: my mouth's so dry, if my life depended on it I couldn't spit." She stepped in the car, sank in the seat. "Sorry, driver. Let's go."

*

TOMATO'S TOMATO MISSING. And: DRUG-CASE ACTRESS BELIEVED GANGLAND VICTIM. In due time, however, the press reported: FLEEING PLAYGIRL TRACED TO RIO. Apparently no attempt was made by American authorities to recover her, and soon the matter diminished to an occasional gossip-column mention; as a news story, it was revived only once: on Christmas Day, when Sally Tomato died of a heart attack at Sing Sing. Months went by, a winter of them, and not a word from Holly. The owner of the brownstone sold her abandoned possessions, the white-satin bed, the tapestry, her precious Gothic chair; a new tenant acquired the apartment, his name was Quaintance Smith, and he entertained as many gentlemen callers of a noisy nature as Holly ever had – though in this instance Madame Spanella did not object, indeed she doted on the young man and supplied filet mignon whenever he had a black eye. But in the spring a postcard came: it was scribbled in pencil, and signed with a lipstick kiss: *Brazil was beastly but Buenos Aires the best. Not Tiffany's, but almost. Am joined at the*

---

6 **gangland** (infml.): Unterwelt.
9 **to recover:** wiederbekommen, wiederzurückholen.
21 **filet mignon:** Lendenfilet.
   black eye: ‚blaues' Auge.
23 **beastly** (infml.): schrecklich, fürchterlich.
24 f. **joined at the hip:** Wortspiel mit *hip-joint* ›Hüftgelenk‹ und *on the hip* ›zum Nachteil‹.

hip with duhvine Señor. Love? Think so. Anyhoo am
looking for somewhere to live (Señor has wife, 7 brats)
and will let you know address when I know it myself. Mille
tendresse. But the address, if it ever existed, never was
5 sent, which made me sad, there was so much I wanted to
write her: that I'd *sold* two stories, had read where the
Trawlers were countersuing for divorce, was moving out
of the brownstone because it was haunted. But mostly, I
wanted to tell about her cat. I had kept my promise; I had
10 found him. It took weeks of after-work roaming through
those Spanish Harlem streets, and there were many false
alarms – flashes of tiger-striped fur that, upon inspection,
were not him. But one day, one cold sunshiny Sunday
winter afternoon, it was. Flanked by potted plants and
15 framed by clean lace curtains, he was seated in the window of a warm-looking room: I wondered what his name
was, for I was certain he had one now, certain he'd
arrived somewhere he belonged. African hut or whatever, I hope Holly has, too.

---

1 **duhvine:** Wortprägung von Holly; gemeint ist vermutl. *divine:* gött-
lich.
Señor (Span.): Herr.
anyhoo (dial.): *anyhow.*
7 **to countersue:** sich gegenseitig verklagen.
8 **to be haunted:** (von einem Geist) heimgesucht werden.
12 **inspection:** Untersuchung, Überprüfung.
15 **lace curtain:** Spitzengardine.

Editorische Notiz

Der englische Text folgt der Ausgabe: Truman Capote, *Breakfast at Tiffany's. A Short Novel and Three Stories*, New York: Random House, 1958. Das Glossar erklärt in der Regel alle Wörter, die über die Wertigkeitsstufe 4 des *Englischen Arbeitswörterbuches* von Alfred Haase (Frankfurt a. M.: Moritz Diesterweg, [7]1979) hinausgehen. Im Zweifelsfall wurde großzügig verfahren, d. h. eher eine Vokabel mehr aufgenommen als dort vorgesehen.

Im Glossar verwendete Abkürzungen

adv.	adverb
AE	American English
arch.	archaic (veraltet)
BE	British English
dial.	dialectal (mundartlich)
fig.	figuratively (übertragen)
Fr.	French
hum.	humorously (scherzhaft)
infml.	informal (umgangssprachlich)
Ital.	Italian
o.s.	oneself
pej.	pejorative (abschätzig)
pl.	plural
Port.	Portuguese
s.o.	someone
Span.	Spanish
s.th.	something
vulg.	vulgar (vulgär, derb)
Yid.	Yiddish

Anmerkungen

1 Louis Comfort Tiffany (1848–1933), amerikanischer Maler, Jugendstilkünstler und Juwelier, gründete das berühmte Juweliergeschäft in Midtown Manhattan an der Südostecke des Central Park (Ecke 57th St. / Fifth Ave.). Hollys extravagantem Wunsch, bei diesem Juwelier zu frühstücken (vgl. S. 47), verdankt die Erzählung ihren Namen.

2 Die East Seventies erstrecken sich als Parallelstraßen in west-östlicher Richtung von der Fifth Avenue zum East River, im Süden und Norden begrenzt von dem Museum der Frick Collection (vgl. Anm. 70) und der den Central Park nördlich des Lake querenden Transverse Road Nr. 1. Der Stadtbezirk ist die Upper East Side.

3 Hollys Nachname bedeutet etwa ›Leichtfuß‹ (von *to go lightly* ›schwebend leicht einhergehen‹) und kann als »telling name« (sprechender, d. h. charakterisierender Name) angesehen werden.

4 Die Lexington Avenue verläuft parallel zwischen der Third Avenue und der Park Avenue. Der Erzähler und Holly wohnen also in unmittelbarer Nähe des Lenox Hill Krankenhauses.

5 William Schwenck Gilbert (1836–1911), englischer Schriftsteller und Librettist, begründete zusammen mit dem englischen Komponisten Arthur Sullivan (1842–1900) den Typ der »Savoy Opera« – benannt nach dem Savoy Theatre in London, wo viele dieser Opern ihre Uraufführung erlebten, z. B. *The Mikado* (1885) und *The Grand Duke* (1896). Diese in Deutschland kaum bekannten Opern sind in englischsprachigen Ländern auch heute noch sehr beliebt.

6 Walter Winchell war ein bekannter Kolumnist.

7 Koloraturen sind Ausschmückungen und Verzierungen einer Melodie mit einer Reihe umspielender Töne, besonders praktiziert in der neapolitanischen, klassischen Oper.

8 Der Central Park (800 m breit und 4,5 km lang) erstreckt sich zwischen Fifth Avenue und Central Park West (Eighth

Avenue) sowie Central Park South (57th Street) und Central Park North (110th Street) und ist eines der wichtigsten Erholungsgebiete der New Yorker.

9 Hollys Karte ist in dem eleganten, förmlichen und anspruchsvollen Stil des französischen Juweliers und Uhrenfabrikanten Cartier gedruckt. Cartier unterhält auch eine Niederlassung an der Fifth Avenue.

10 »21-Club« ist der Name eines eleganten Nachtclubs der vierziger Jahre in Midtown Manhattan; er leitet sich vermutlich von »17+4« her.

11 Die 51st Street liegt in der Nähe des Waldorf Astoria Hotels in Midtown Manhattan.

12 »P. J. Clark's Saloon«, heute eine Gaststättenkette, war damals ein volkstümliches und bekanntes Lokal in Midtown Manhattan.

13 Der Begriff bezeichnet ursprünglich jemanden, der mit seiner Habe durch das Land zieht. Hier ist ein bekanntes australisches Volkslied gemeint.

14 Diese Zigarettenmarke trägt den amerikanischen Slang-Ausdruck für ein Fünfcentstück als Namen. *picayune* ist abgeleitet von der alten, spanischen Münze im Wert eines halben Real, die in Louisiana und anderen Südstaaten lange im Umlauf war; im übertragenen Sinn bedeutet es etwa ›Kleinigkeit‹, ›Nichtigkeit‹.

15 Cole Porter (1893–1964) war ein amerikanischer Komponist und Jazzmusiker. Sein Musical *Kiss Me Kate* (1948) ist noch heute weltbekannt. Kurt Weill (1900–50) war ein deutscher Komponist, der 1933 nach Amerika auswanderte und in New York starb. Mit Bert Brecht zusammen schrieb er *Die Dreigroschenoper* (1928). In Amerika komponierte er auch von der Jazz-Musik beeinflußte Filmmusik.

16 Das Musical *Oklahoma!* von Richard Rodgers und Oscar Hammerstein III wurde 1943 uraufgeführt. Zur Funktion der Orts- und Zeitverweise in *Breakfast at Tiffany's* vgl. Nachwort, S. 154.

17 Der belgische Romanschriftsteller George Simenon (geb.

1903) wurde vor allem durch seine Kriminalromane mit dem Kommissar Maigret bekannt.

18 William Saroyan (geb. 1908) ist ein amerikanischer Autor von Kurzgeschichten mit alltäglichen Themen und lebensbejahender Grundeinstellung.

19 Ernest Hemingway (1898–1961), einer der bekanntesten Schriftsteller des 20. Jahrhunderts, erhielt 1954 den Nobelpreis für Literatur. Seine berühmtesten Werke sind *A Farewell to Arms* (1925), *Death in the Afternoon* (1932), *The Green Hills of Africa* (1935), *For Whom the Bell Tolls* (1940) und *The Old Man and the Sea* (1952) sowie die Kurzgeschichtensammlungen *Men without Women* (1927) und *Winner Take Nothing* (1933).

20 William Somerset Maugham (1874–1965) ist ein englischer Schriftsteller, der vor allem naturalistische und sozialkritische Prosa geschrieben hat, so etwa *Liza of Lambeth* (1897), *Of Human Bondage* (1915) und *The Razor's Edge* (1944).

21 Name des Staatsgefängnisses von New York im Hudson-Tal nahe der Stadt Ossining (früher Sing Sing).

22 Das Jiddische ist als aus dem Mittelhochdeutschen abgeleitete Sprache der Juden vor allem in Osteuropa weit verbreitet und wird erst in neuerer Zeit allmählich durch die Staatssprache Israels, das aus dem Hebräischen stammende Iwrith, ersetzt.

23 Die auch heute noch in Süditalien – vornehmlich auf Sizilien – einflußreiche Verbrecherorganisation hat einen starken Zweig in den USA, wo außerdem noch u. a. die »Blackhand« und »Cosa Nostra« existieren.

24 Ähnlich »McDonald's« heute ist »Hamburg Heaven« der Name einer Restaurantkette, in der vornehmlich »Hamburger« serviert werden.

25 Delikatessengeschäft für extravagante Luxuslebensmittel an der Madison Avenue (Nr. 340 und 683, also nahe der 44th St. und der 62nd St.).

26 Stadtteil und Name der Rennbahn von Los Angeles.

27 Margaret Sullavan (1911–60) war eine in den dreißiger Jah-

ren populäre amerikanische Filmschauspielerin (z. B. *Little Man What Now?*, 1934).

28 Cecil B. de Mille (1881–1951) war ein amerikanischer Filmregisseur, Gary Cooper (1901–61) ein berühmter amerikanischer Filmschauspieler.

29 David O. Selznick (1902–65), amerikanischer Filmproduzent, wurde durch den Film *Gone with the Wind* (1939) weltberühmt.

30 Die Engländerin Unity Mitford (1914–48) war für kurze Zeit mit Hitler befreundet.

31 Der nördliche Teil von Yorkville ist das traditionelle Wohngebiet der Deutschen und liegt in der Gegend der East 86th Street zwischen Lexington Avenue und East River.

32 Die russische Schauspielerin Maria Ouspenskaya (1876 bis 1949) wanderte 1923 nach Amerika aus.

33 Für seine vielen chinesischen Restaurants und Geschäfte bekanntes Chinesenviertel in Downtown Manhattan zwischen Chatham Square und Canal Street in der Nähe der Manhattan Bridge über den East River.

34 Mag arbeitet als Fotomodell für eine seriöse amerikanische Frauenzeitschrift, *Harper's Bazaar*.

35 Hotel an der Ecke Madison Avenue und 55th Street im Rockefeller Center. Auch heute noch leben nicht wenige Amerikaner in Hotels statt in eigenen Wohnungen.

36 Das »Barbizon-Plaza« (106 Central Park South) ist auch heute noch ein Hotel der Luxusklasse mit 1200 Betten.

37 Der »Stork Club« war ein renommierter Nachtclub der oberen Zehntausend.

38 Portugiesisch ist die Landessprache Brasiliens. Das Land wurde 1600 von dem Spanier Balbao entdeckt, aber kurz darauf schon portugiesische Kolonie.

39 Die Dienerinnen der ägyptischen Königin Cleopatra (69–30 v. Chr.) waren Charmian und Iras.

40 Pracht- und Luxusstraße Manhattans und heute eine der Hauptverkehrsadern in nord-südlicher Richtung.

41 In Anlehnung an den Kunststil des Impressionismus, der um 1870 in Frankreich entstand, bezeichnet der Ausdruck hier

einen ganz kurzfristigen und oberflächlichen Eindruck, der keine grundsätzlichen und tiefen Erkenntnisse vermittelt.

42 Der Vorabend des Allerheiligentages am 1. November (»Halloween«) wird in englischsprachigen Ländern mit Umzügen Maskierter gefeiert. Ursprünglich begann nach dem alten keltischen Kalender das Neue Jahr am 1. November, und der letzte Tag des alten Jahres war die Hexennacht.

43 Namen bekannter Nachtclubs der vierziger Jahre in Midtown Manhattan.

44 Nachtclub der High Society in New York.

45 Der nach einer der reichsten Familien der USA benannte Platz liegt in Midtown Manhattan am Schnittpunkt der Fifth Avenue und der 50th Street. John Davidson Rockefeller (1839–1937) beherrschte den amerikanischen Erdölmarkt und gründete wertvolle Stiftungen für Wissenschaft und Wohlfahrt. Sein Sohn John Davidson Rockefeller jr. (1874 bis 1960) setzte sowohl das wirtschaftliche als auch das mäzenatische und soziale Werk seines Vaters fort. Nelson Aldrich Rockefeller schließlich (1908–79) wurde als Politiker Gouverneur des Staates New York (1958–74) und Vizepräsident unter Präsident Gerald Ford von 1974–76.

46 Die Insel Nantucket, ein amerikanisches Walfangzentrum, ist der Südostküste von Massachusetts vorgelagert.

47 Die karibischen Inseln (große und kleine Antillen, Bahamas) verdanken ihren Namen der fälschlichen Annahme von Christoph Columbus, er sei 1492 in Indien gelandet.

48 Am weitesten südlich gelegene Stadt der USA am Westende der Halbinsel Florida.

49 Dieser Roman von Emily Brontë (1818–48) aus dem Jahr 1847 zählt zu den Höhepunkten der viktorianischen Romankunst. Er handelt vornehmlich von der Liebe zwischen Catherine (Cathy) Earnshaw und dem Findling Heathcliff sowie zwischen Catherines Tochter Cathy und Hareton Earnshaw. Holly meint die Verfilmung von 1939.

50 Diese Kreuzung liegt ganz nahe der den Central Park querenden Transverse Road Nr. 3. Die Madison Avenue ist in der Höhe des Central Park für ihre Kunstgalerien bekannt.

51 Tulip ist ein kleines Dorf in Texas (County Fannin).

52 Da das Eisenbahnnetz in den USA nicht mehr gut ausgebaut ist, wird der Fernverkehr auf dem Luftweg oder per Straße abgewickelt. »Greyhounds« (wörtl.: Windhunde) werden die Überlandbusse genannt, die die Rolle der Eisenbahnen als Massenfernverkehrsmittel übernommen haben.

53 Der »Independence Day« erinnert an den 4. Juli 1776, an dem die Unabhängigkeitserklärung der dreizehn Gründerstaaten der USA verkündet wurde.

54 Gemeint ist eine Bergkette in Pennsylvania, die Doc Golightly auf der Rückreise nach Texas durchquert. Die bekannteren Blue Mountains – bis zu 2773 m hoch – liegen in den Bundesstaaten Oregon und Washington im äußersten Nordwesten der USA.

55 Brooklyn, das ursprünglich nach dem bei Utrecht gelegenen holländischen Ort Breuckelen benannt wurde, liegt an der Südwestspitze von Long Island und ist der bevölkerungsreichste »borough« (Großstadtbezirk) von New York mit 2,6 Millionen Einwohnern. Brooklyn, von Manhattan durch den East River getrennt, ist vorwiegend eine Wohnstadt mit hohem Italiener- und Farbigenanteil.

56 Greenwich Village liegt zwischen Broadway und Hudson sowie zwischen Houston Street und 14th Street. Dieser Teil von Downtown Manhattan mit seinem Zentrum, dem Washington Square, ist das Künstlerviertel von New York.

57 *PM* war eine bekannte kulturell orientierte Zeitschrift.

58 Renommiertes (heute zu Sotheby's of London gehöriges) Auktionshaus an der Madison Avenue (nahe der 77th Street).

59 William Randolph Hearst (1863–1951) war ein bekannter amerikanischer Verleger von bis zu vierzig Boulevardzeitungen mit einem eigenen Nachrichtendienst.

60 In der »Modern Library« des renommierten New Yorker Verlags Random House sind viele Klassiker der englischsprachigen Literatur erschienen.

61 Das an der Ecke von Fifth Avenue und 82nd Street im Cen-

tral Park gelegene Museum ist eine der bedeutendsten Kunstsammlungen der Welt.

62 Die Firma Waring ist ein bekannter Küchengerätehersteller.

63 Der römische Kaiser Nero (37–68) war für seinen extravaganten, manchmal degenerierten Geschmack bekannt. Er soll im Jahr 64 selbst für den Brand Roms verantwortlich gewesen sein.

64 Ein auch heute noch existierendes Sprachlehrunternehmen, das stark mediengestützt arbeitet.

65 Jawaharlal Nehru (1889–1964), indischer Staatsmann und erster Ministerpräsident des unabhängigen Indien (1947 bis 1964), wurde vor allem für seine Politik des passiven Ungehorsams gegen die britische Kolonialmacht bekannt.

66 Der Politiker Wendell Willkie (1892–1944) trat im Kampf um das Präsidentenamt 1940 erfolglos gegen Franklin D. Roosevelt an.

67 Greta Garbo (1905–1990), schwedische Schauspielerin, wurde in den dreißiger Jahren zum Leinwandidol einer ganzen Generation (*Gösta Berling, Anna Karenina, Das göttliche Weib, Mata Hari, Menschen im Hotel, Ninotschka* usw.). Sie lebte zuletzt zurückgezogen in New York.

68 Die in den Jahren 1867–83 von den deutschstämmigen Architekten Johann August und Washington Röbling erbaute Brücke verbindet in Höhe des südlichen Anfangs der Park Avenue die New Yorker »boroughs« Manhattan und Brooklyn.

69 Der Reitstall befand sich unmittelbar an der Transverse Road Nr. 1 am Westrand des Central Park.

70 Das Duke Mansion (Ecke Fifth Ave. / East 78th St.) wurde 1901 für James B. Duke, den Gründer von British American Tobacco (BAT), erbaut. Dieses Herrenhaus beherbergt heute das Institute of Fine Arts der New York University. Die Frick Collection (Ecke Fifth Ave. / East 70th St.) erinnert an den Stahlbaron und Kunstsammler Clay Frick (1849–1919) und ist als Sammlung europäischer Gemälde und Skulpturen aus dem 14. bis 19. Jahrhundert bekannt.

Das »Pierre Hotel« (Ecke Fifth Ave. / East 61st St.) im Besitz der Getty-Familie ist auch heute noch ein bekanntes Hotel der Luxusklasse, wie auch das »Plaza Hotel« (Ecke Fifth Ave. / East 59th St.).

71 Von diesen Zeitungen existiert heute nur noch die *New York Daily News*.

72 Das Hotel »Seabord« liegt im Theater District südwestlich des Central Park.

73 Mit der Übernahme des deutschen Begriffs »Führer« wird zur Zeit der Romanhandlung 1943/44 das Verwerfliche der Mafia-Organisation besonders unterstrichen.

74 Cefalù ist eine kleine Hafenstadt an der Nordküste Siziliens, etwa 80 km östlich von Palermo.

75 Prominentenvorort von Los Angeles.

76 Gorillaähnliches Riesenungeheuer, das in dem gleichnamigen Film (1933) New York in Angst und Schrecken versetzte.

77 Der Flughafen Idlewild (eingeweiht 1948, aber schon vorher in Betrieb) heißt heute John F. Kennedy International Airport und liegt im Stadtteil Queens an der Jamaica Bay.

78 Diese Namen bezeichnen wahrscheinlich bekannte, erstklassige Restaurants in New York.

79 Möglicherweise Name eines Kriminellen.

80 Traditionelles Tanzlokal in 239 West 52nd Street.

81 Wahrscheinlich kleiner Ort im Bundesstaat Mississippi.

82 Carey ist auch heute noch eine bekannte Mietwagenfirma in New York.

83 Vorwiegend von Puerto Ricanern bewohnter New Yorker Stadtteil, der sich zwischen der Amsterdam Avenue und der Park Avenue sowie in der Gegend der West 96th Street erstreckt.

Literaturhinweise

[Anon.:] »Monstrum unter edlen Schwänen«, in: *Der Spiegel* 42 (1988), H. 27, S. 152–155.

Baldanza, F., »Plato in Dixie«, in: *Georgia Review* 12 (1958) S. 150–167.

Berger, Yves, »Truman Capote«, in: *Critique* (Paris) 15 (1959) S. 491–507.

Burgess, Anthony, »Puck of the Beautiful People«, in: *The Observer*, 21. 8. 1988.

Capote, Truman, »A *Playboy* Interview: Truman Capote«, in: *Playboy* 15 (1968), H. 3, S. 51–62, 160–170.

– / Lambert, J. W., »Fulfilment and the Non-Fiction Novel«, in: *The Sunday Times*, 8. August 1965, S. 31.

Clarke, Gerald, *Capote: A Biography*, New York 1988.

Dommergues, Pierre, »Romanciers américains de l'Innocence«, in: *Les Langues Modernes* 59 (1965) S. 54–59.

Frankel, Haskel, »Truman Capote: The Author«, in: *Saturday Review*, 22. Januar 1966, S. 36 f.

Garson, Helen S., *Truman Capote*, New York 1980.

Gingrich, Arnold, »Gossip As an Art Form«, in: *Esquire* 85, 9. Mai 1976.

Goad, Craig M., »Daylight and Darkness, Dream and Delusion: The Works of Truman Capote«, in: *Emporia State Research Studies* 16 (1967) S. 5–57.

Hassan, Ihab H., »Birth of a Heroine«, in: *Prairie Schooner* 34 (1960) S. 78–83.

Hellman, John, »The Nature and Mode of the New Journalism«, in: *Genre* 13 (1980) S. 517–529.

Howe, Irving, Rez. von: Truman Capote, *Breakfast at Tiffany's*, in: *Partisan Review* 26 (1959) S. 130–136.

Levine, Paul, »Truman Capote: The Revelation of the Broken Image«, in: *Virginia Quarterly Review* 34 (1958) S. 600 bis 617.

– Rez. von: Truman Capote, *Breakfast at Tiffany's*, in: *Georgia Review* 13 (1959) S. 350–352.

Littlejohn, David, »Capote Collected«, in: *Commonweal* 78 (1963) S. 187 f.

Mengeling, Marvin E., »*Other Voices, Other Rooms:* Oedipus Between the Covers«, in: *American Imago* 19 (1962) S. 361–374.

Moravia, Alberto, »Two American Writers«, in: *Sewanee Review* 68 (1960) S. 473–481.

Mouton, Jean, *Littérature et sang-froid. Un récit véridique de Truman Capote pose des questions au roman*, Paris 1977.

Nance, William N., *The Worlds of Truman Capote*, New York 1970.

Peden, William, Rez. von: Truman Capote, *Breakfast at Tiffany's*, in: *Virginia Quarterly Review* 35 (1959) S. 153–160.

Pini, Richard, »Fiction et Réalité chez Truman Capote«, in: *Les Langues Modernes* 69 (1969) S. 176–185.

Pizer, Donald, »Documentary Narrative As Art«, in: *Journal of Modern Literature* 2 (1972) S. 105–118.

Reed, Kenneth T., *Truman Capote*, Boston 1981.

Stelzmann, Rainulf A., »Schein, Sünde und Wahrheit. Die Welt Truman Capotes«, in: *Stimmen der Zeit* 201 (1983) S. 85–94.

Wall, Richard / Craycraft, Carl L., »A Checklist of Works about Truman Capote«, in: *Bulletin of the New York Public Library* 121 (1967) S. 165–172.

Nachwort

I

Truman Capote war lange Zeit eine schillernde Gestalt der literarischen und gesellschaftlichen Welt der Vereinigten Staaten, und sein ungeheurer Erfolg könnte fast wie die Erfüllung des materiellen Aspekts des »American Dream«, des Aufstiegs vom Tellerwäscher zum Millionär, aussehen, wäre da nicht auch sein jammervoller Tod 1984 in den Niederungen des Alkoholismus und der Tablettenabhängigkeit, und wären da nicht auch die Zweifel, ob das recht schmale Lebenswerk des Autors seinem eigenen Anspruch gerecht wird, zu den ganz Großen der Literatur zu zählen.[1] Im nachhinein erscheint sein Leben wie der verzweifelte Versuch, die Nachteile und Entbehrungen seiner Jugend auf möglichst vielen Ebenen zu kompensieren: er suchte Anerkennung als Autor, als Wegweiser eines »neuen« literarischen Typus – der *nonfiction novel*, er fühlte sich am wohlsten in der Gesellschaft der Reichen und Mächtigen, denen er zuweilen rauschende Feste ausrichtete – wie etwa das am 29. 11. 1966 aus Anlaß des spektakulären Erfolgs von *In Cold Blood*[2] im Plaza Hotel von New York, an dem mehrere hundert Gäste teilnahmen, unter ihnen:

> »Rose Kennedy, Princess Lee Radziwill, Mrs. Stavros Niarchos, Lynda Bird Johnson, Mr. and Mrs. Henry Ford II, Princess d'Arenberg, Countess Gianni Agnelli, Alfred Gwynne Vanderbilt, Margaret Truman Daniels, Countess Rudi Crespi and Undersecretary of State Nicholas Katzenbach.«[3]

---

1 Vgl. Truman Capote, »A *Playboy* Interview«, in: *Playboy* 15, Heft 3 (1968) S. 168, und Anthony Burgess, »Puck of the Beautiful People«, in: *The Observer*, 21. 8. 1988.

2 In den ersten zwei Jahren seit Erscheinen wurden 800000 gebundene und 2,5 Millionen broschierte Exemplare verkauft, was einen Erlös von $ 3,5 Millionen bedeutete; vgl. dazu Capote (Anm. 1) S. 51.

3 Capote (Anm. 1) S. 52; vgl. auch »Monstrum unter edlen Schwänen«, in: *Der Spiegel* 42 (1988), H. 27, S. 152.

Capotes gesellschaftlicher und materieller Erfolg war ebenso groß und spektakulär wie sein Niedergang plötzlich und schäbig:

> »The decay – urinating on the floor, lying swathed in his own excrement – is horrifying. He wanted to die and believed that the seeds of the wish had been sown in an unhappy childhood. He may have been right.«[4]

Capote wurde am 30. 9. 1924 in New Orleans als Sohn der Eheleute Arch und Lilli Mae Persons geboren, wuchs aber nach der frühen Scheidung seiner Eltern und der Wiederverheiratung seiner Mutter mit dem Kubaner Joseph Garcia Capote bei Verwandten in Alabama und später in New York bzw. Connecticut auf,[5] wo er mit nur mäßigem Erfolg Schulen besuchte, obwohl ihm ein Intelligenztest außergewöhnliche geistige Fähigkeiten attestierte. Schon in früher Jugend versuchte er sich als Autor; sein Erstlingsroman *Old Mr. Busybody* überlebte die ersten Fortsetzungen in einer lokalen Zeitung jedoch nicht, weil die Leser ohne Mühe die Vorlagen für die vier Hauptcharaktere erkannten und es zu erheblichen Protesten kam. Schon hier erkennt man eines der für Capotes Werke typischen Merkmale: die starke Durchdringung des Fiktionalen mit nichtfiktionalen Elementen, den Versuch einer Symbiose von fiktionaler Literatur und Journalismus. *Other Voices, Other Rooms* (1948), Capotes erster großer Erfolg, ist nicht nur nach Capotes eigenem Bekunden eine literarische Verarbeitung seiner Jugend: »The book is a prose poem in which I have taken my own emotional problems and transformed them into psychological symbols [...]. So the central theme of the book was my search for my father.«[6]

Sowohl in diesem Werk als auch in dem 1951 erschienenen Roman *The Grass Harp* werden Fiktionales und Nichtfiktionales noch in – wenn auch abnehmender – Anlehnung an den traditionellen Literaturtyp der Autobiographie miteinander

4 So Burgess (Anm. 1).

5 Vgl. William N. Nance, *The Worlds of Truman Capote*, New York 1970, S. 12 und S. 14.

6 Capote (Anm. 1) S. 53.

verknüpft. Beiden Romanen gemeinsam ist auch das Phantastische, Traumartige; jedoch folgt auf die groteske und bedrückende imaginative Verarbeitung von Jugenderlebnissen in *Other Voices, Other Rooms* in *The Grass Harp* ein leichterer, lebensbejahender Grundtenor. In beiden Romanen dominiert ganz eindeutig die fiktionale Phantasiewelt über die nichtfiktionale, autobiographische Faktenwelt. In dem 1956 erschienenen *The Muses Are Heard*, einem Bericht über das Rußlandgastspiel eines Opernensembles mit George Gershwins Oper *Porgy and Bess*, verhält es sich dagegen umgekehrt. Hier überwiegt naturgemäß das journalistische Element. Erst *In Cold Blood* (1966) stellt Capotes gelungenen Versuch dar, Journalismus und Schriftstellerei am Beispiel der literarischen Verarbeitung des in sechsjähriger Arbeit bis in alle Einzelheiten recherchierten Mordfalls an einer Farmerfamilie aus dem Mittleren Westen miteinander zu verknüpfen.[7]

II

In diesem Spannungsfeld aus Phantasie und Realität, Groteske und Heiterkeit, Autobiographie und Fiktionalität, Anspruch und Wirklichkeit findet auch *Breakfast at Tiffany's* (1958) seinen Platz. Daher ist es auch nicht weiter verwunderlich, daß die ersten Rezensionen seiner Erzählung kein klares Bild bieten. Irving Howe spricht von einem »slight thing but neither precious nor exhibitionist«,[8] bewundert den Stil Capotes, beklagt sich über einige »dimestore exotica« der zweiten Hälfte des Romans und erkennt in Holly Golightly das »terrifying ultimate in rootlessness: the human creature without bonds, notions, responsibilities, delusions«;[9] William Peden dagegen spricht von einer letztlich ermüdenden, sogar langweiligen Geschichte, einer bloß »deftly written novella about an amoral hillbilly-

---

7 Zu Recht umstritten bleibt jedoch Capotes Anspruch, mit diesem Werk ein neues Genre geschaffen zu haben. Versuche in ähnlicher Richtung hat es immer wieder seit Begründung der Gattung Roman gegeben; vgl. etwa Daniel Defoes *A Journal of the Plague Year* (1723) und Henry Fieldings *The Voyage to Lisbon* (1755).

8 Irving Howe, Rez. von: Truman Capote, *Breakfast at Tiffany's*, in: *Partisan Review* 26 (1959) S. 131.

9 Ebd.

turned-glamour girl«, das sich weigere, erwachsen zu werden.[10]
Paul Levine schließlich sieht Ambiguität als das Charakteristikum des Werks; es sei eine »controlled extravaganza«;[11] Holly -
»a hard-headed romantic, a pragmatic idealist«[12] – sei zugleich
eine »enchanting childlike adventuress«[13] und auf der letztlich
vergeblichen Suche nach einem »real-life place«.[14] Damit verkörpere sie eines der Zentralmotive des Nachkriegsromans, die
Suche nach Liebe in all ihren Formen: »sexual, homosexual,
asexual, perhaps even spiritual«.[15]

III

Levines Hinweis auf den Doppelcharakter Hollys und des
gesamten Romans hat sich in der späteren Capote-Kritik zu
Recht weitgehend durchgesetzt. Die oberflächliche Leichtigkeit des Tons, die Komik der Szenen kann nicht die existentielle
Unsicherheit der Charaktere verbergen. Der noch jugendliche
Erzähler etwa steht angesichts der drohenden Einberufung zum
Wehrdienst im Zweiten Weltkrieg (S. 89) und seiner materiell
ungesicherten Situation – er verliert schon bald sein erste feste
Stellung (ebd.) und muß auf finanzielle Unterstützung durch
seine Familie hoffen (S. 101) – weitgehend perspektivenlos da,
ist auf der Suche nach »experience«; und der steinreiche, gänzlich unreife und unfertige Rusty Trawler hofft vergeblich auf
eine Mutterfigur, die ihn durch das Leben geleitet.
In besonderem Maße trifft die Bezeichnung ambivalent jedoch
auf Holly Golightly, die ihrer Visitenkarte entsprechend leicht
und unbeschwert durch die Welt zu reisen scheint, ohne sich um
moralische Konventionen oder allgemein anerkannte Verhaltensnormen zu scheren. Leichthin nimmt sie die Dienste ihrer
Mitbewohner in Anspruch, weil sie gewohnheitsmäßig ihre

10 Vgl. William Peden, Rez. von: Truman Capote, *Breakfast at Tiffany's*, in: *Virginia Quarterly Review* 35 (1959) S. 157.
11 Paul Levine, Rez. von: Truman Capote, *Breakfast at Tiffany's*, in: *Georgia Review* 13 (1959) S. 350.
12 Ebd., S. 351.
13 Ebd.
14 Ebd., S. 352.
15 Ebd.

Hausschlüssel verlegt oder vergißt; aus Angst vor einem zudringlichen Liebhaber fällt sie über die Feuertreppe bei dem Erzähler ein und übernachtet bei ihm; sie spannt Mag Wildwood, mit der sie ihre Wohnung teilt, ohne weiteres den Freund aus, und sie gibt sich schließlich in entwaffnender Naivität als Nichte eines Gangsterbosses aus, dessen kodierte Botschaften sie jeweils nach ihren Besuchen bei diesem Verbrecher im Zuchthaus weitergibt, womit sie ohne ihr Wissen eine Schlüsselrolle im Drogengeschäft spielt. Ihren Lebensunterhalt bestreitet sie im wesentlichen mit den großzügigen Geldspenden, die ihre Begleiter ihr – in der meist enttäuschten Hoffnung auf eine Liebesnacht – für den Besuch der Damentoilette überreichen;[16] nach ihrer Freilassung gegen Kaution flieht sie heimlich aus dem Land, um ihr Flugticket nach Rio de Janeiro nicht verfallen zu lassen, mit der entwaffnenden Begründung: »Besides, I've never been to Brazil« (S. 123). Alle diese Belege reichen jedoch bei weitem nicht hin, um sie als leichtlebige Dame der Halbwelt abzustempeln. Ihr Charakter entzieht sich einer präzisen, eindeutigen Definition ebenso wie ihre äußere Erscheinung. »Chic thinness« und »breakfast-cereal air of health« halten sich die Waage, ihr Gesicht ist »beyond childhood, yet this side of belonging to a woman« (S. 15). Die gleiche Ambivalenz kennzeichnet auch ihr eigentliches Wesen. Ihrem Verlangen nach Freiheit und Ungebundenheit steht ihre Suche nach Schutz und Geborgenheit gegenüber, ihrer Amoralität im Sinne bürgerlicher Vorstellungen ihre private Moral, ihrem zur Schau getragenen Selbstbewußtsein die Angst vor dem Leben und dem Tod. Sie ist zugleich Holly und die noch vierzehnjährige Lulamae Barnes:

> »Even though I kept telling him: But, Doc, I'm not fourteen any more, and I'm not Lulamae. But the terrible part is (and I realized it while we were standing there) I am. I'm still stealing turkey eggs and running through a brier patch« (S. 87 f.).

---

16 Holly kann keinesfalls mit dem Begriff Prostituierte hinreichend charakterisiert werden, wie es etwa Craig M. Goad tut in seinem Aufsatz »Daylight and Darkness, Dream and Delusion: The Works of Truman Capote,« in: *Emporia State Research Studies* 16 (1967) S. 39.

Freiheit begehrt Holly aber nicht nur für sich allein, sondern sie ist auch bereit, anderen ihre Freiheit zu lassen, nichts und niemanden mit dem Anspruch auf Besitz an sich zu binden. Daher verkörpert für sie auch das Vogelbauer den Inbegriff des Gefangenseins, und sie verlangt von dem Erzähler: »Promise you'll never put a living thing in it« (S. 72). Auch mit ihrer zugelaufenen, herrenlosen Katze verbindet sie kein Besitzverhältnis: »[...] we don't belong to each other: he's an independent, and so am I. I don't want to own anything until I know I've found the place where me and things belong together« (S. 48). Besonders der letzte Teil des Zitats offenbart jedoch Hollys eigentliche, tiefe Sehnsucht nach einem Ort, an dem sie sich mit ihrer Umwelt eins weiß, an dem sie sich geborgen fühlt wie bei ihrem Bruder Fred oder vorübergehend bei dem Erzähler (S. 32 f.), ohne dafür ihre Freiheit aufgeben zu müssen: »If I could find a real-life place that made me feel like Tiffany's, then I'd buy some furniture and give the cat a name« (S. 49).[17] Fände Holly am Schluß der Erzählung ihr Tiffany, d. h. Ruhe, Geborgenheit, Sicherheit und Freiheit, dann wäre der Vorwurf, es handle sich bei dieser Erzählung um ein »slight thing« oder ein »brilliant trifle«,[18] wohl gerechtfertigt, aber eben dies ist mehr als zweifelhaft. Noch zwölf Jahre nach ihrer Abreise aus New York wird sie Weihnachten 1956 im zentralafrikanischen Busch gesehen – offensichtlich noch immer auf der Suche (S. 8), während ihre Katze schnell ans Ziel gelangt:

»Flanked by potted plants and framed by clean lace curtains, he was seated in the window of a warm-looking room: I wondered what his name was, for I was certain he had one now, certain he'd arrived somewhere he belonged. African hut or whatever, I hope Holly has, too« (S. 134).

Hollys existentielle Angst – ihre »mean reds« und ihr Schrecken vor der »fat woman« (S. 118, 132 f.), der Inkarnation des Todes – kulminiert in ihren letzten Worten: »I'm very scared, Buster. Yes, at last. Because it could go on forever. Not knowing what's

17 Vgl. dazu Yves Berger, »Truman Capote«, in: *Critique* (Paris) 15 (1959) S. 499, und Ihab H. Hassan, »Birth of a Heroine«, in: *Prairie Schooner* 34 (1960) S. 81.
18 Howe (Anm. 8) S. 131, und Burgess (Anm. 1).

yours until you've thrown it away«« (S. 132). Vor diesem Hintergrund ist auch Capotes Irritation über die Verfilmung seines Romans mit Audrey Hepburn zu verstehen, in dem die existentielle Not Hollys und auch der zeitliche Hintergrund – die Kriegsjahre 1943 bis 1945 – unterschlagen werden: »The film became a mawkish valentine to New York City and Holly, as a result, was thin and pretty, whereas it should have been rich and ugly«.[19]
Noch ein anderer Aspekt trägt zu der Ernsthaftigkeit des Romans trotz des spielerisch leichten Tons bei. Hollys Verhaltens- und Moralkodex spricht zwar allen konventionellen, »normalen« Maßstäben hohn, deckt sich aber mit ihrer »natürlichen« (S. 61), d. h. nicht vom gesellschaftlichen Umfeld geprägten, privaten Auffassung von Ehrlichkeit und Moral. »Law-type«-Ehrlichkeit lehnt sie zugunsten der »unto-thyself-type«-Ehrlichkeit (S. 99) ab und läßt als Norm für zwischenmenschliches Verhalten nur gelten, wie der Mitmensch sie behandelt (S. 124 f.). Daß sie mit diesem privaten, a-sozialen Moralkodex in der Gesellschaft nicht bestehen kann, ist nicht weiter erstaunlich, fällt aber als Vorwurf eher auf eben diese Gesellschaft zurück. Mit ihren »quixotic ideas of hope, sincerity, truth«[20] kämpft sie gegen die oberflächlichen Konventionen eines O. J. Berman, eines Rusty Trawler oder ihres brasilianischen Freundes José wie gegen Windmühlenflügel an. Die lediglich am materiellen Erfolg orientierte Gesellschaft bietet der suchenden Holly keinen Halt, sie bleibt unterwegs, rastlos getrieben und ohne Ziel, »on the road«, wie es der programmatische und ein Jahr vor Capotes Werk erschienene Roman Jack Kerouacs ausdrückt, der wohl am deutlichsten das Lebensgefühl der Beat-Generation der späten fünfziger Jahre verkörpert. Trotz des Scheiterns ihrer Suche nach einem »real-life place« rückt Holly mit ihrer Rebellion gegen das Normale in die Nähe eines Vorbildes, auch wenn sie keine überzeugende Lösung anzubieten hat, wie etwa Goad behauptet, der ihr eine gesellschaftsreformerische Funktion zuschreibt.[21] Sie ist ein Vorbild allenfalls deswegen, weil sie

19 Capote (Anm. 1) S. 169.
20 Hassan (Anm. 17) S. 62; vgl. auch Nance (Anm. 5) S. 123.
21 Vgl. Goad (Anm. 16) S. 39.

die Notwendigkeit der Rebellion erkannt hat, auch wenn ihre faustische[22] Suche letztlich fehlschlägt.[23]

IV

Die Relevanz der Geschichte für die amerikanische Gesellschaft wird unterstrichen durch die autobiographischen, biographischen und journalistischen Elemente des Romans. Unter diesem Blickwinkel betrachtet, ist *Breakfast at Tiffany's* nur eine wichtige Etappe auf Capotes Weg zu *In Cold Blood*, seiner *nonfiction novel*. Das Lokalkolorit in *Breakfast at Tiffany's* entspricht bis in kleinste Details dem des New York der späten Kriegsjahre, die erwähnten Straßen, Hotels, Nachtclubs und Restaurants existieren größtenteils noch heute. Die Hauptfigur Holly fußt, wenn man Capotes Worten glauben darf, weitgehend auf dem Schicksal einer deutschen Einwanderin, die zu Beginn des Krieges als Siebzehnjährige aus Deutschland floh, ein ähnliches Leben wie die fiktive Holly führte und wie diese letztmalig nach dem Krieg in einem afrikanischen Dschungeldorf gesehen wurde.[24] Capote geht es allerdings nicht um dieses Einzelschicksal allein. Wichtiger ist ihm, daß dieses Mädchen die Unrast und ungesicherte Existenz des Individuums in New York darstellt: »She was such a symbol of all these girls who come to New York and spin in the sun for a moment like May flies and then disappear«.[25] Auch sich selbst bezieht Capote in dieses ungesicherte Leben mit ein. Wie Capote hat der Erzähler am 30. September Geburtstag (S. 101), ist etwa im gleichen Alter, wohnt erst seit kurzem ohne Angehörige in New York (S. 3) und tritt seine erste feste Stellung dort an.[26] Wichtiger als diese offensichtlichen autobiographischen Elemente ist jedoch die Einbeziehung seiner schriftstellerischen Ambitionen. Wie Holly ist auch der Erzähler auf der Suche – nicht in erster Linie nach materiellem Erfolg, eher nach literarischer Anerkennung

22 Vgl. Hassan (Anm. 17) S. 81.
23 Vgl. Berger (Anm. 17) S. 507, und Levine (Anm. 11) S. 352.
24 Capote (Anm. 1) S. 162.
25 Vgl. ebd., S. 161.
26 Vgl. Nance (Anm. 5) S. 14.

(S. 3, 62) und menschlichen Beziehungen. Die Anerkennung Hollys bleibt ihm versagt, weil seine Geschichten ihr nichts sagen (S. 25 f.). Mit ihrem ehemaligen Agenten Berman ist sie sich einig: »»[. . .] you're on the wrong track. Negroes and children: who cares? [. . .] *Description*. It doesn't *mean* anything«« (S. 74). Hingegen verbindet ihn mit Holly eine tiefe menschliche, gänzlich unerotische Beziehung, die mit dem konventionellen Konzept der Liebe nur unzulänglich charakterisiert ist. Der Erzähler ist während der zweijährigen engen Freundschaft, die im übrigen auch zum Zeitpunkt des Erzählens zwölf Jahre später noch fortlebt, der einzige Halt für Holly; er allein verfolgt im Zusammenhang mit ihr keine persönlichen Interessen, er stellt keine Bedrohung ihrer Unabhängigkeit und Freiheit dar. Statt dessen gelingt es ihm, ihr zumindest vorübergehend Schutz und Geborgenheit zu geben, ihr den geliebten Bruder zu ersetzen. Wenn er diese Funktion nicht auf Dauer erfüllen kann, dann deswegen, weil, wie Berger schreibt, keine dauerhafte Beziehung zwischen Charakteren sowie zwischen Charakteren und der Welt bestehen kann.[27] *Breakfast at Tiffany's* ist nicht die Geschichte vom Scheitern eines exzentrischen Individuums noch gar die Verherrlichung einer amerikanischen Version der Geisha;[28] vielmehr ist es die fiktionale Darstellung der Suche des Individuums nach Selbstverwirklichung und zugleich sozialem Kontakt in einer oberflächlichen und feindlichen Umwelt. Wer den Roman nur wegen seiner Unkonventionalität und seiner komischen Passagen liest, verkennt das grundsätzliche Anliegen Truman Capotes.

Herbert Geisen

---

27 Vgl. Berger (Anm. 17) S. 497.
28 Vgl. Capote (Anm. 1) S. 161.

Inhalt

Fremdsprachentexte

IN RECLAMS UNIVERSAL-BIBLIOTHEK

Amerikanische Literatur

Afro-American Short Stories. 167 S. UB 9276

Woody Allen: Hannah and Her Sisters. 208 S. 4 Abb. UB 9277

American Film Stories. 144 S. UB 9029

American Crime Stories. (Collier, Ellin, MacDonald, Cain, Slesar, Millar) 167 S. UB 9268

American Short Stories of the 19th Century. 300 S. UB 9034

L. Frank Baum, The Wonderful Wizard of Oz. 211 S. UB 9001

Ray Bradbury: Fahrenheit 451. 247 S. UB 9270

Ernest Callenbach: Ecotopia. 367 S. UB 9030

Truman Capote: Breakfast at Tiffany's. 157 S. UB 9241

Raymond Chandler: The Big Sleep. 379 S. UB 9009 – Killer in the Rain. 128 S. UB 9198

Contemporary American Short Stories. (Vonnegut, Merwin, Barth, Barthelme, Updike, Godwin, Pynchon, Oates, Graham) 155 S. UB 9206

William Faulkner: Barn Burning. 64 S. UB 9043

F. Scott Fitzgerald: The Great Gatsby. 255 S. UB 9242

Charlotte Perkins Gilman: The Yellow Wallpaper. 48 S. UB 9224

Winston Groom: Fornest Gump. 301 S. UB 9033

Patricia Highsmith: A Shot from Nowhere. Six Stories. 160 S. UB 9262

Henry James: Daisy Miller. 139 S. UB 9251

Kiss Me, Kate. A Musical. (Book Samuel and Bella Spewack, Music and Lyrics Cole Porter) 181 S. UB 9263

Jack London: Three Stories. 91 S. UB 9225

Herman Melville: Bartleby. 88 S. UB 9190

Philipp Reclam jun. Stuttgart